SHORT STORY STUDY

A Critical Anthology

Compiled by

A. J. SMITH

UNIVERSITY COLLEGE, SWANSEA

and

W. H. MASON

MANCHESTER GRAMMAR SCHOOL

With a foreword by
LORD JAMES OF RUSHOLME

LONDON
EDWARD ARNOLD (PUBLISHERS) LTD.

FIRST PUBLISHED 1961
REPRINTED 1962

PRINTED IN GREAT BRITAIN IN THE CITY OF OXFORD
AT THE ALDEN PRESS

FOREWORD

Argue as we may about over-specialization, its reality, its causes, and the steps that we should take to correct it, most of us would agree in encouraging any attempt to induce our pupils both to read more and to read more intelligently. Across the gulfs that are supposed, often wrongly, to divide the scientist from the arts student, one of the most important bridges that we can build is a common enjoyment of a body of good literature. One is, indeed, often tempted to think that if once we have persuaded our pupils to read widely and even to buy books for themselves, the problems of general education are over. This is not, of course, strictly true. Reading can too easily be yet another method of passing the time, as the ubiquity of *Readers Digests* in any railway carriage only too clearly testifies. If reading is to be more than a mild soporific it must contain some element of discrimination and must bring into play an exercise of critical appreciation. The problem for the teacher is to lead his pupil to see that to be aware of what a writer is trying to do, even to make some effort to understand how he does it, does not lessen enjoyment but enhances it.

The editors of this collection of short stories have made, it seems to me, a most successful attempt to solve this problem. The stories that they have chosen can certainly be enjoyed. It is easy to imagine the reader of *Tickets Please* being lured on to tackle *Sons and Lovers*, or even *Paste* being for some member of the science sixth a first step on the glorious pilgrimage to *The Ambassadors*. But something more than passive enjoyment is asked of the reader. The questions asked and the judgments demanded are acute enough to make the reader realize that he must be something more than a recipient, and that reading good literature is an active business, an enterprise demanding more from him than the ability to follow the printed word. I can well imagine senior students finding this anthology an introduction to a world in which distinctions between specialists become meaningless, the world of the intelligent enjoyment of good writing. As the work of two very good teachers of English it should commend itself to

3

those concerned with the needs of students of very varying kinds. And if those who use the book are stimulated by disagreement with the selection of authors or the comments upon them to make their own anthology and to ask their own questions, then, one feels, the deeper intentions of the compilers will have been fulfilled.

JAMES OF RUSHOLME

CONTENTS

INTRODUCTION

THIS BOOK IS intended to meet the need of the teacher of young men and women for recent, or near-recent, writing of quality and maturity, which will at the same time be amenable to intensive tutorial study both in respect of matter and of length. Many such teachers will have realized the possibilities of the short story and sought to use specimens of their own choosing, well beyond the scope of the stock school anthology: the editors have simply brought together some pieces which they for their part have handled with success, in the form in which they would have liked to present them to their pupils. Their hope is that others will find the resultant volume as useful as they themselves would have done.

These stories were originally worked over with groups ranging in special interest from mathematics to English literature, and in type from sixth form to adult education. In general, apart from the obvious desirability of wide variety, four considerations have governed the choice, and the direction of the accompanying matter. They are as follows: the need (*a*) to "provide a bridge" (in Gilbert Highet's phrase) from school or university to the world outside, and from youth to maturity (*b*) to stimulate close and intelligent reading, and to indicate the proper use of literature as a mature discipline (*c*) to afford some understanding of the ground of such literary attitudes as tragedy, comedy, melodrama, pathos, sentimentality, and invite reflection on the wider bearing of these (*d*) to inculcate sound critical approaches, and impart familiarity with the vocabulary, tools, and method of literary criticism. Of course, the best use of the book will be that which keeps all four ends in sight, but it should adequately serve the turn of the tutor who seeks no more than to put before his pupils some representative work of acknowledged masters in this kind.

As regards the method of the book, which might be thought novel, the editors have aimed to carry out a normal teaching programme in rather more detail than would commonly be possible to the class tutor, and in doing so to provide the student with a full apparatus for his own pondering. The ancillary matter is intended not to supply packaged judgments — God forbid — but to offer the necessary background and equipment for independent inquiry. The commentaries, in particular, may need here and there to be helped out by the teacher; and they will have served some part of their purpose if they occasionally suggest a line of approach to him. Otherwise, the student should gain by a demonstration with readily apprehensible material of what it is hoped may prove — at this level — a fairly rigorous critical scrutiny. But naturally, it is open to a reader to use the editors as whipping-boys or, if he wishes, ignore their intrusions altogether.

1

HENRY JAMES

1843-1916

It would not be too much to say that what is most important in the life of Henry James is not the events or even the personal relationships — though these cannot be ignored — but the stages in his conception of the art of writing. For he was a man dedicated to his craft. Quite early in life (James was born in New York in 1843) he felt himself a lonely child, although he had a happy, leisured and cultured home. An injury to his back prevented his serving in the American Civil War and accentuated his feeling that it was not in the world of affairs that he was to find his way of life. In 1870 the death of his beloved cousin Minny Temple at the age of twenty-four deeply affected James, for as he said: "I always looked forward with a certain eagerness to the day when I should have regained my natural lead, and one friendship, on my part, at least, might have become more active and masculine." And so Henry James, whilst always a man who delighted in company — he was one of the great "diners-out" of his day — essentially withdrew into the world of creative writing.

As a boy and as a young man he had travelled in Europe. In 1875 he made the critical decision — to live in Europe: "I have made my choice, and God knows that I have no time to lose." He finally settled at Rye, in Sussex, becoming a naturalized British subject in 1915, some six months before his death in February 1916.

James had begun writing when a young man at the Harvard Law School and his productivity remained remarkable for more than forty years. Novels, stories, travel sketches, criticism, plays (his incursion into drama in the 1890s was grievously unsuccessful) came from him with an ever-deepening subtlety and psychological complexity — a progression that proved too much for many who prefer the relative straightforwardness of early works like *Roderick Hudson* (1876) to the labyrinthine, yet controlled, intricacy of later novels like *The Golden Bowl* (1904), of which George Sampson writes (*Concise Cambridge History of Literature*) "those who can read it can read everything he wrote".

It is difficult to represent the genius of Henry James by a *short* story for the genre that proved most congenial to his gifts was the "long short story", such as *The Spoils of Poynton, The Aspern Papers* or, the best known of all, *The Turn of the Screw*. For what James was seeking, in novel or story, was ever determined by (the phrase is his own) "the law of entire expression". The implications of this ruling concept are manifold. Time and again James tells us of the importance he attached to perceiving the possibilities of a given situation, to letting it work within the mind subject to further and further analysis until "the smothered rapture and the obscure victory" of triumphant achievement. The virtues of James's writing are therefore those of the dedicated artist: exquisite sensibility, moral and psychological, directed by a controlling intelligence that saw form and style as indispensable constituents of that "entire expression" which is the distinguishing feature of his work.

Suggested Reading: *Daisy Miller* (1878); *The Portrait of a Lady* (1881); *The Aspern Papers* (1888); *The Spoils of Poynton* (1896); *The Turn of the Screw* (1898); *The Wings of a Dove* (1902); *The Ambassadors* (1903).

*   *   *

Paste

"I'VE found a lot more things," her cousin said to her the day after the second funeral; "they're up in her room — but they're things I wish *you'd* look at."

The pair of mourners, sufficiently stricken, were in the garden of the vicarage together, before luncheon, waiting to be summoned to that meal, and Arthur Prime had still in his face the intention, she was moved to call it rather than the expression, of feeling something or other. Some such appearance was in itself of course natural within a week of his stepmother's death, within three of his father's; but what was most present to the girl, herself sensitive and shrewd, was that he seemed somehow to brood without sorrow, to suffer without what she in her own case would have called pain. He turned away from her after this last speech — it was a good deal his habit to drop an observation and leave her to pick it up without assistance. If the vicar's widow, now in her turn finally translated, had not really belonged to him it was not for want of her giving herself, so far as he ever would take her; and she had lain for three days all alone at the end of the passage, in the great cold chamber of hospitality, the dampish, greenish room where visitors slept and where several ladies of the parish had, without effect, offered, in pairs and successions, piously to watch with her. His personal connection with the parish was now slighter than ever, and he had really not waited for this opportunity to show the ladies what he thought of them. She felt that she herself had, during her doleful month's leave from Bleet, where she was governess, rather taken her place in the same snubbed order; but it was presently, none the less, with a better little hope of coming in for some remembrance, some relic, that she went up to look at the things he had spoken of, the identity of which, as a confused cluster of bright objects on a table in the darkened room, shimmered at her as soon as she had opened the door.

They met her eyes for the first time, but in a moment, before touching them, she knew them as things of the theatre, as very much too fine to have been, with any verisimilitude, things of the vicarage. They were too dreadfully good to be true, for her aunt had had no jewels to speak of, and these were coronets and girdles, diamonds, rubies and sapphires. Flagrant tinsel and glass, they looked strangely vulgar, but if, after the first queer shock of them, she found herself taking them up, it was for the very proof, never yet so distinct to her, of a far-off faded story. An honest widowed cleric with a small son and a large sense of Shakespeare had, on a brave latitude of habit as well as of taste — since it implied his having in very fact dropped deep into the "pit" — conceived for an obscure actress, several years older than himself, an admiration of which the prompt offer of his reverend name and hortatory hand was the sufficiently candid sign. The response had perhaps, in those dim years, in the way of eccentricity, even bettered the proposal, and Charlotte, turning the tale over, had long since drawn from it a measure of the career renounced by the undistinguished *comédienne* — doubtless also tragic, or pantomimic, at a pinch — of her late uncle's dreams. This career could not have been eminent and must much more probably have been comfortless.

"You see what it is — old stuff of the time she never liked to mention."

Our young woman gave a start; her companion had, after all, rejoined her and had apparently watched a moment her slightly scared recognition. "So I said to myself," she replied. Then, to show intelligence, yet keep clear of twaddle: "How peculiar they look!"

"They look awful," said Arthur Prime. "Cheap gilt, diamonds as big as potatoes. These are the trappings of a ruder age than ours. Actors do themselves better now."

"Oh now," said Charlotte, not to be less knowing, " actresses have real diamonds."

"Some of them." Arthur spoke drily.

"I mean the bad ones — the nobodies too."

"Oh, some of the nobodies have the biggest. But mamma wasn't of that sort."

"A nobody?" Charlotte risked.

"Not a nobody to whom somebody — well, not a nobody with diamonds. It isn't all worth, this trash, five pounds."

There was something in the old gewgaws that spoke to her, and she continued to turn them over. "They're relics. I think they have their melancholy and even their dignity."

Arthur observed another pause. "Do you care for them?" he then asked. "I mean," he promptly added, "as a souvenir."

"Of you?" Charlotte threw off.

"Of me? What have I to do with it? Of your poor dead aunt who was so kind to you," he said with virtuous sternness.

"Well, I would rather have them than nothing."

"Then please take them," he returned in a tone of relief which expressed somehow more of the eager than of the gracious.

"Thank you." Charlotte lifted two or three objects up and set them down again. Though they were lighter than the materials they imitated they were so much more extravagant that they struck her in truth as rather an awkward heritage, to which she might have preferred even a matchbox or a penwiper. They were indeed shameless pinchbeck. "Had you any idea she had kept them?"

"I don't at all believe she *had* kept them or knew they were there, and I'm very sure my father didn't. They had quite equally worked off any tenderness for the connection. These odds and ends, which she thought had been given away or destroyed, had simply got thrust into a dark corner and been forgotten."

Charlotte wondered. "Where then did you find them?"

"In that old tin box" — and the young man pointed to the receptacle from which he had dislodged them and which stood on a neighbouring chair. "It's rather a good box still, but I'm afraid I can't give you *that*."

The girl gave the box no look; she continued only to look at the trinkets. "What corner had she found?"

"She hadn't 'found' it," her companion sharply insisted; "she had simply lost it. The whole thing had passed from her mind. The box was on the top shelf of the old schoolroom closet, which, until one put one's head into it from a step-ladder, looked, from below, quite cleared out. The door is narrow and the part of the closet to the left goes well into the wall. The box had stuck there for years."

Charlotte was conscious of a mind divided and a vision vaguely troubled, and once more she took up two or three of the subjects of this revelation; a big bracelet in the form of a gilt serpent with many twists and beady eyes, a brazen belt studded with emeralds and rubies, a chain, of flamboyant architecture, to which at the Theatre Royal, Little Peddlington, Hamlet's mother had probably been careful to attach the portrait of the successor to Hamlet's father. "Are you very sure they're not really worth something? Their mere weight alone — !" she vaguely observed, balancing a moment a royal diadem that might have crowned one of the creations of the famous Mrs Jarley.

But Arthur Prime, it was clear, had already thought the question over and found the answer easy. "If they had been worth anything to speak of she would long ago have sold them. My father and she had unfortunately never been in a position to keep any considerable value locked up." And while his companion took in the obvious force of this he went on with a flourish just marked enough not to escape her: "If they're worth anything at all — why, you're only the more welcome to them."

Charlotte had now in her hand a small bag of faded, figured silk — one of those antique conveniences that speak to us, in the terms of evaporated camphor and lavender, of the part they have played in some personal history; but, though she had for the first time drawn the string, she looked much more at the young man than at the questionable treasure it appeared to contain. "I shall like them. They're all I have."

"All you have — ?"

"That belonged to her."

He swelled a little, then looked about him as if to appeal — as against her avidity — to the whole poor place. "Well, what else do you want?"

"Nothing. Thank you very much." With which she bent her eyes on the article wrapped, and now only exposed, in her superannuated satchel — a necklace of large pearls, such as might once have graced the neck of a provincial Ophelia and borne company to a flaxen wig. "This perhaps *is* worth something. Feel it." And she passed him the necklace, the weight of which she had gathered for a moment into her hand.

He measured it in the same way with his own but remained quite detached. "Worth at most thirty shillings."

"Not more?"

"Surely not if it's paste?"

"But *is* it paste?"

He gave a small sniff of impatience. "Pearls nearly as big as filberts?"

"But they're heavy," Charlotte declared.

"No heavier than anything else." And he gave them back with an allowance for her simplicity. "Do you imagine for a moment they're real?"

She studied them a little, feeling them, turning them round.

"Mightn't they possibly be?"

"Of that size — stuck away with that trash?"

"I admit it isn't likely," Charlotte presently said. "And pearls are so easily imitated."

"That's just what — to a person who knows — they're not. These have no lustre, no play."

"No — they *are* dull. They're opaque."

"Besides," he lucidly inquired, "how could she ever have come by them?"

"Mightn't they have been a present?"

Arthur stared at the question as if it were almost improper. "Because actresses are exposed — ?" He pulled up, however, not saying to what, and before she could supply the deficiency had, with the sharp ejaculation of "No, they mightn't!" turned his back on her and walked away. His manner made her feel that she had probably been wanting in tact, and before he returned to the subject, the last thing that evening, she had satisfied herself of the ground of his resentment. They had been talking of her departure the next morning, the hour of her train and the fly that would come for her, and it was precisely these things that gave him his effective chance. "I really can't allow you to leave the house under the impression that my stepmother was at *any* time of her life the sort of person to allow herself to be approached — "

"With pearl necklaces and that sort of thing?" Arthur had made for her somehow the difficulty that she couldn't show him she understood him without seeming pert.

It at any rate only added to his own gravity. "That sort of thing, exactly."

"I didn't think when I spoke this morning–but I see what you mean."

"I mean that she was beyond reproach," said Arthur Prime.

"A hundred times yes."

"Therefore if she couldn't, out of her slender gains, ever have paid for a row of pearls — "

"She couldn't, in that atmosphere, ever properly have had one? Of course she couldn't. I've seen perfectly since our talk," Charlotte went on, "that that string of beads isn't even, as an imitation, very good. The little clasp itself doesn't seem even gold. With false pearls, I suppose," the girl mused, "it naturally wouldn't be."

"The whole thing's rotten paste," her companion returned as if to have done with it. "If it were *not*, and she had kept it all these years hidden — "

"Yes?" Charlotte sounded as he paused.

"Why, I shouldn't know what to think!"

"Oh, I see." She had met him with a certain blankness, but adequately enough, it seemed, for him to regard the subject as dismissed; and there was no reversion to it between them before, on the morrow, when she had with difficulty made a place for them in her trunk, she carried off these florid survivals.

At Bleet she found small occasion to revert to them and, in an air charged with such quite other references, even felt, after she had lain them away, much enshrouded, beneath various piles of clothing, as if they formed a collection not wholly without its note of the ridiculous. Yet she was never, for the joke, tempted to show them to her pupils, though Gwendolen and Blanche, in particular, always wanted, on her return, to know what she had brought back; so that without an accident by which the case was quite changed they might have appeared to enter on a new phase of interment. The essence of the accident was the sudden illness, at the last moment, of Lady Bobby, whose advent had been so much counted on to spice the five days' feast laid out for the coming of age of the eldest son of the house; and its equally marked effect was the despatch of a pressing message, in quite another direction, to Mrs Guy, who, could she by a miracle be secured—she was always engaged ten parties deep—might be trusted to supply, it was believed, an element of exuberance scarcely less active. Mrs Guy was already known to several of the visitors already on the scene, but she was not yet known to our young lady, who found her, after many wires and counterwires had at last determined the triumph of her arrival, a strange, charming little red-haired, black-dressed woman with the face of a baby and the authority of a commodore. She took on the spot the discreet, the exceptional young governess into the confidence of her designs and, still more, of her doubts; intimating that it was a policy she almost always promptly pursued.

"Tomorrow and Thursday are all right," she said frankly to Charlotte on the second day, "but I'm not half satisfied with Friday."

"What improvement then do you suggest?"

"Well, my strong point, you know, is *tableaux vivants*."

"Charming. And what is your favourite character?"

"Boss!" said Mrs Guy with decision; and it was very markedly under that ensign that she had, within a few hours, completely planned her campaign and recruited her troop. Every word she uttered was to the point, but none more so than after a general survey of their equipment, her final inquiry of Charlotte. She had been looking about, but half appeased, at the muster of decoration and drapery. "We shall be dull. We shall want more colour. You've nothing else?"

Charlotte had a thought. "No — I've *some* things."

"Then why don't you bring them?"

The girl hesitated. "Would you come to my room?"

"No," said Mrs Guy — "bring them tonight to mine."

So Charlotte, at the evening's end, after candlesticks had flickered through brown old passages bedward, arrived at her friend's door with the burden of her aunt's relics. But she promptly expressed a fear. "Are they too garish?"

When she had poured them out on the sofa Mrs Guy was but a minute, before the glass, in clapping on the diadem. "Awfully jolly — we can do Ivanhoe!"

"But they're only glass and tin."

"Larger than life they are, *rather*! — which is exactly what, for tableaux, is wanted. *Our* jewels, for historic scenes, don't tell — the real thing falls short. Rowena must have rubies as big as eggs. Leave them with me," Mrs Guy continued — "they'll inspire me. Goodnight."

The next morning she was in fact — yet very strangely — inspired. "Yes, *I'll* do Rowena. But, I don't, my dear, understand."

"Understand what?"

Mrs Guy gave a very lighted stare, "How you come to have such things."

Poor Charlotte smiled. "By inheritance."

"Family jewels?"

"They belonged to my aunt, who died some months ago. She was on the stage a few years in early life, and these are a part of her trappings."

"She left them to you?"

"No; my cousin, her stepson, who naturally has no use for them, gave them to me for remembrance of her. She was a dear kind thing, always so nice to me, and I was fond of her."

Mrs Guy had listened with visible interest. "But it's *he* who must be a dear kind thing!"

Charlotte wondered. "You think so?"

"Is *he*," her friend went on, "also 'always so nice' to you?"

The girl at this, face to face there with the brilliant visitor in the deserted breakfast-room, took a deeper sounding. "What is it?"

"Don't you know?"

Something came over her. "The pearls — ?" But the question fainted on her lips.

"Doesn't *he* know?"

Charlotte found herself flushing. "They're *not* paste?"

"Haven't you looked at them?"

She was conscious of two kinds of embarrassment. "*You* have?"

"Very carefully."

"And they're real?"

Mrs Guy became slightly mystifying and returned for all answer: "Come again, when you've done with the children, to my room."

Our young woman found she had done with the children, that morning, with a promptitude that was a new joy to them, and when she reappeared before Mrs Guy this lady had already encircled a plump white throat with the only ornament, surely, in all the late Mrs Prime's — the effaced Miss Bradshaw's — collection, in the least qualified to raise a question. If Charlotte had never yet once, before the glass, tied the string of pearls about her own neck, this was because she had been capable of no such condescension to approved "imitation"; but she had now only to look at Mrs Guy to see that, so disposed, the ambiguous objects might have passed for frank originals. "What in the world have you done to them?"

"Only handled them, understood them, admired them and put them on. That's what pearls want; they want to be worn — it wakes them up. They're alive, don't you see? How *have* they been treated? They must have been buried, ignored, despised. They were half dead. Don't you *know* about pearls?" Mrs Guy threw off as she fondly fingered the necklace.

"How *should* I? Do *you*?"

"Everything. These were simply asleep, and from the moment I really touched them — well," said the wearer lovingly, "it only took one's eye!"

"It took more than mine — though I did just wonder; and then

Arthur's," Charlotte brooded. She found herself almost panting. "Then their value — ?"

"Oh, their value's excellent."

The girl, for a deep moment, took another plunge into the wonder, the beauty and mystery, of them "Are *you sure?*"

Her companion wheeled round for impatience. "Sure? For what kind of an idiot, my dear, do you take me?"

It was beyond Charlotte Prime to say. "For the same kind as Arthur — and as myself," she could only suggest. "But my cousin didn't know. He thinks they're worthless."

"Because of the rest of the lot? Then your cousin's an ass. But what — if, as I understood you, he gave them to you — has he to do with it?"

"Why, if he gave them to me as worthless and they turn out precious — "

"You must give them back? I don't see that — if he was such a fool. He took the risk."

Charlotte fed, in fancy, on the pearls which, decidedly, were exquisite, but which at the present moment somehow presented themselves much more as Mrs Guy's than either Arthur's or as her own. "Yes — he did take it; even after I had distinctly hinted to him that they looked to me different from the other pieces."

"Well, then!" said Mrs Guy with something more than triumph — with a positive odd relief.

But it had the effect of making our young woman think with more intensity. "Ah, you see he thought they couldn't be different, because — so peculiarly — they shouldn't be."

"Shouldn't? I don't understand."

"Why, how would she have got them?" — so Charlotte candidly put it.

"She? Who?" There was a capacity in Mrs Guy's tone for a sinking of persons — !

"Why, the person I told you of: his stepmother, my uncle's wife — among whose poor old things, extraordinarily thrust away and out of sight, he happened to find them."

Mrs Guy came a step nearer to the effaced Miss Bradshaw. "Do you mean she may have stolen them?"

"No. But she had been an actress."

"Oh, well then," cried Mrs Guy, "wouldn't that be just how?"

"Yes, except that she wasn't at all a brilliant one, nor in receipt of large pay." The girl threw off a nervous joke. "I'm afraid she couldn't have been our Rowena."

Mrs Guy took it up. "Was she very ugly?"

"No. She may very well, when young, have looked rather nice."

"Well, then!" was Mrs Guy's sharp comment and fresh triumph.

"You mean it was a present? That's just what he so dislikes the idea of her having received — a present from an admirer capable of going such lengths."

"Because she wouldn't have taken it for nothing? *Speriamo* — that she wasn't a brute. The 'length' her admirer went was the length of a whole row. Let us hope she was just a little kind!"

"Well," Charlotte went on, "that she was 'kind' might seem to be shown by the fact that neither her husband, nor his son, nor I, his niece, knew or dreamed of her possessing anything so precious; by her having kept the gift all the rest of her life beyond discovery — out of sight and protected from suspicion."

"As if, you mean" — Mrs Guy was quick — "she had been wedded to it and yet was ashamed of it? Fancy," she laughed while she manipulated the rare beads, "being ashamed of *these!*"

"But you see she had married a clergyman."

"Yes, she must have been 'rum'. But at any rate he had married *her*. What did he suppose?"

"Why, that she had never been of the sort by whom such offerings are encouraged."

"Ah, my dear, the sort by whom they are *not* — !" But Mrs Guy caught herself up. "And her stepson thought the same?"

"Overwhelmingly."

"Was he, then, if only her stepson — "

"So fond of her as that comes to? Yes; he had never known, consciously, his real mother, and, without children of her own, she was very patient and nice with him. And *I* liked her so," the girl pursued, "that at the end of ten years, to 'give her away' — "

"Is impossible to you? Then don't !" said Mrs Guy with decision.

"Ah, but if they're real I can't keep them!" Charlotte, with her eyes on them, moaned in her impatience. "It's too difficult."

"Where's the difficulty, if he has such sentiments that he would rather sacrifice the necklace than admit it, with the presumption it carries with it, to be genuine? You've only to be silent."

"And keep it? How can *I* ever wear it?"

"You'd have to hide it, like your aunt?" Mrs Guy was amused. "You can easily sell it."

Her companion walked round her for a look at the affair from behind. The clasp was certainly, doubtless intentionally, misleading, but everything else was indeed lovely. "Well, I must think. Why didn't *she* sell them?" Charlotte broke out in her trouble.

Mrs Guy had an instant answer. "Doesn't that prove what they secretly recalled to her? You've only to be silent!" she ardently repeated.

"I must think — I must think!"

Mrs Guy stood with her hands attached but motionless. "Then you want them back?"

As if with the dread of touching them Charlotte retreated to the door. "I'll tell you tonight."

"But may I wear them?"

"Meanwhile?"

"This evening — at dinner."

It was the sharp, selfish pressure of this that really, on the spot, determined the girl; but for the moment, before closing the door on the question, she only said: "As you like!"

They were busy much of the day with preparation and rehearsal, and at dinner, that evening, the concourse of guests was such that a place among them for Miss Prime failed to find itself marked. At the time the company rose she was therefore alone in the schoolroom, where, towards eleven o'clock, she received a visit from Mrs Guy. This lady's white shoulders heaved, under the pearls, with an emotion that the very red lips which formed, as if for the full effect, the happiest opposition of colour, were not slow to translate. "My dear, you should have seen the sensation — they've had a success!"

Charlotte, dumb for a moment, took it all in. "It *is* as if they knew it — they're more and more alive. But so much the worse for both of us! I can't," she brought out with an effort, "be silent."

"You mean to return them?"

"If I don't I'm a thief."

Mrs Guy gave her a long, hard look: what was decidedly not of the baby in Mrs Guy's face was a certain air of established habit in the eyes. Then, with a little jerk of her head and a backward reach of her bare beautiful arms, she undid the clasp and, taking off the necklace, laid it on the table. "If you do, you're a goose."

"Well, of the two — !" said our young lady, gathering it up with a sigh. And as if to get it, for the pang it gave, out of sight as soon as possible, she shut it up, clicking the lock, in the drawer of her own little table; after which, when she turned again, her companion, without it, looked naked and plain. "But what will you say?" it then occurred to her to demand.

"Downstairs — to explain?" Mrs Guy was, after all, trying at least to keep her temper. "Oh, I'll put on something else and say that the clasp is broken. And you won't of course name *me* to him," she added.

"As having undeceived me? No — I'll say that, looking at the thing more carefully, it's my own private idea."

"And does he know how little you really know?"

"As an expert — surely. And he has much, always, the conceit of his own opinion."

"Then he won't believe you — as he so hates to. He'll stick to his judgment and maintain his gift, and we shall have the darlings back!" With which reviving assurance Mrs Guy kissed her good night.

She was not, however, to be gratified or justified by any prompt event, for, whether or no paste entered into the composition of the ornament in question, Charlotte shrank from the temerity of despatching it to town by post. Mrs Guy was thus disappointed of the hope of seeing the business settled — "by return", she had seemed to expect — before the end of the revels. The revels, moreover, rising to a frantic pitch, pressed for all her attention, and it was at last only in the general confusion of leave-taking that she made, parenthetically, a dash at her young friend.

"Come, what will you take for them?"

"The pearls? Ah, you will treat with my cousin."

Mrs Guy, with quick intensity, lent herself. "Where then does he live?"

"In chambers in the Temple. You can find him."

"But what's the use, if *you* do neither one thing nor the other?"

"Oh, I shall do the 'other'," Charlotte said: "I'm waiting till I go up. You want them so awfully?" She curiously, solemnly, again sounded her.

"I'm dying for them. There's a special charm in them — I don't know what it is: they tell so their history."

"But what do you know of that?"

"Just what they themselves say. It's all *in* them — and it comes out. They breathe a tenderness — they have the white glow of it. My dear," hissed Mrs Guy in supreme confidence and as she buttoned her glove — "they're things of love!"

"Oh!" our young woman vaguely exclaimed.

"They're things of passion!"

"Mercy!" she gasped, turning short off. But these words remained, though indeed their help was scarce needed, Charlotte being in private face to face with a new light, as she by this time felt she must call it, on the dear dead, kind, colourless lady whose career had turned so sharp a corner in the middle. The pearls had quite taken their place as a revelation. She might have received them for nothing—admit that; but she couldn't have kept them so long and so unprofitably hidden, couldn't have enjoyed them only in secret, for nothing; and she had mixed them, in her reliquary, with false things, in order to put curiosity and detection off the scent. Over this strange fact poor Charlotte interminably mused: it became more touching, more attaching for her than she could now confide to any ear. How bad, or how happy — in the sophisticated sense of Mrs Guy and the young man at the Temple — the effaced Miss Bradshaw must have been to have had to be so mute! The little governess at Bleet put on the necklace now in secret sessions; she wore it sometimes under her dress; she came to feel, verily, a haunting passion for it. Yet in her penniless state she would have parted with it for money; she gave herself also to dreams of what in this direction it would do for her. The sophistry of her so often saying to herself that Arthur had after all

pronounced her welcome to any gain from his gift that might accrue
— this trick remained innocent, as she perfectly knew it for what it was.
Then there was always the possibility of his — as she could only
picture it — rising to the occasion. Mightn't he have a grand mag-
nanimous moment? — mightn't he just say: "Oh, of course I couldn't
have afforded to let you have it if I had known; but since you *have*
got it, and have made out the truth by your own wit, I really can't
screw myself down to the shabbiness of taking it back?"

She had, as it proved, to wait a long time — to wait till, at the end
of several months, the great house of Bleet had, with due deliberation,
for the season, transferred itself to town; after which, however, she
fairly snatched at her first freedom to knock, dressed in her best and
armed with her disclosure, at the door of her doubting kinsman. It
was still with doubt and not quite with the face she had hoped that he
listened to her story. He had turned pale, she thought, as she produced
the necklace, and he appeared, above all disagreeably affected. Well,
perhaps there was reason, she more than ever remembered; but what
on earth was one, in close touch with the fact, to do? She had laid out
the pearls on his table, where, without his having at first put so much
as a finger to them, they met his hard, cold stare.

"I don't believe in them," he simply said at last.

"That's exactly then," she returned with some spirit, "what I
wanted to hear!"

She fancied that at this his colour changed; it was indeed vivid to
her afterwards — for she was to have a long recall of the scene — that she
had made him quite angrily flush. "It's a beastly unpleasant imputation,
you know!" — and he walked away from her as he had always walked
at the vicarage.

"It's none of *my* making, I'm sure," said Charlotte Prime. "If you're
afraid to believe they're real — "

"Well?" — and he turned, across the room, sharp round at her.
"Why, it's not my fault."

He said nothing more, for a moment, on this; he only came back to the
table. "They're what I originally said they were. They're rotten paste."

"Then I may keep them?"

"No. I want a better opinion."

"Than your own?"

"Than *your* own." He dropped on the pearls another queer stare, then, after a moment, bringing himself to touch them, did exactly what she had herself done in the presence of Mrs Guy at Bleet— gathered them together, marched off with them to a drawer, put them in and clicked the key.

"You say I'm afraid," he went on as he again met her; "but I shan't be afraid to take them to Bond Street."

"And if the people say they're real — ?"

He hesitated — then had his strangest manner. "They won't say it! They shan't!"

There was something in the way he brought it out that deprived poor Charlotte, as she was perfectly aware, of any manner at all. "Oh!" she simply sounded, as she had sounded for her last word to Mrs Guy; and, within a minute, she had taken her departure.

A fortnight later she received a communication from him, and towards the end of the season one of the entertainments in Eaton Square was graced by the presence of Mrs Guy. Charlotte was not at dinner, but she came down afterwards and this guest, on seeing her, abandoned a very beautiful young man on purpose to cross and speak to her. The guest had on a lovely necklace and had apparently not lost her habit of overflowing with the pride of such ornaments.

"Do you see?" She was in high joy.

They were indeed splendid pearls — so far as poor Charlotte could feel that she knew, after what had come and gone, about such mysteries. Charlotte had a sickly smile. "They're almost as fine as Arthur's."

"Almost? Where, my dear, are your eyes? They *are* 'Arthur's!' "

After which, to meet the flood of crimson that accompanied her young friend's start: "I tracked them — after your folly, and, by miraculous luck, recognized them in the Bond Street window to which he had disposed of them."

"*Disposed* of them?" the girl gasped. "He wrote me that I had insulted his mother and that the people had shown him he was right — had pronounced them utter paste."

Mrs Guy gave a stare. "Ah, I told you he wouldn't bear it! No. But I had, I assure you," she wound up, "to drive my bargain!"

Charlotte scarce heard or saw; she was full of her private wrong. "He wrote me," she panted, "that he had smashed them."

Mrs Guy could only wonder and pity. "He's really morbid!" But it was not quite clear which of the pair she pitied; though Charlotte felt really morbid too after they had separated and she found herself full of thought. She even went the length of asking herself what sort of a bargain Mrs Guy had driven and whether the marvel of the recognition in Bond Street had been a veracious account of the matter. Hadn't she perhaps in truth dealt with Arthur directly? It came back to Charlotte almost luridly that she had had his address.

COMMENTARY

Some writers make greater demands than others on their readers. We often read a story or a novel and know as we are reading that if our attention is distracted or relaxed it will not greatly matter. Little of importance will be lost; the dialogue, for example, can be picked up ten lines further on and we shall not feel that anything of critical significance has been missed. That is not the way of Henry James. Few writers require the continuous co-operation of their reader to the degree that he does. For this reason you will frequently hear someone say: "Oh, I can't read Henry James. He takes so long to say so little. And I never seem able to keep up with what his people are saying." Such a remark can come only from one who has not *read* the Master. For James delighted in translating into his stories and his novels the finest nuances of feeling, and, above all, of moral sensibility. It is *that*, first of all, you should be prepared to discern and to respond to in *Paste*. (Note the *quality* of the different reactions of the three protagonists to the possibility of the pearls being genuine and the consequent bearing of this on the acquisition of the pearls by the dead woman.) You should also see how what is loosely if conveniently called "character drawing" is done by James in an altogether subtler manner than by most writers: it is the personality of his *dramatis personae* expressing itself in conduct. First, then, observe that with regard to his persons James focuses our attention only upon that which matters directly for the purpose of the story — their moral selves.

In the years preceding the writing of *Paste* (1900) Henry James had tried, but unsuccessfully, to write for the theatre. Though the complete failure of his plays was a great disappointment to him, there is no doubt that his art as a writer of stories and of novels gained much from the discipline and formal values that drama imposes. *Paste* is a story unmistakably dramatic in structure. (Think of appropriate programme titles for the Acts into which the story falls. How many are there? Where can we clearly mark the end of Act I? Where would you place the beginning of the last Act?) Once you have seen this dramatic form within the story, you will also notice the pattern and the balance in the distribution of the action — Charlotte and Arthur; Charlotte and Mrs Guy; Charlotte and Arthur again.

Continuity and development are essential to the short story, though both these terms need to be interpreted appropriately for each story. (Find examples — you may find some in this collection — where, for instance, development may be thought of rather as in depth than in sequence of events.) Consider now how naturally and economically James achieves this requisite feature. In connection with continuity the handling of time in a story is always worth observing; you might collect references to show how James "moves" his narrative. A skilful writer rarely maintains a uniformity of rate in the progress of his story. You may find it interesting to think of the musical terms appropriate to the different *tempi* to be found in the successive stages of *Paste*.

It is when you turn your attention to the dialogue that you should be aware of that distinguishing quality of James's writing referred to in the first paragraph of this note. At first, reading the conversation of Charlotte and Arthur or of Charlotte and Mrs Guy, you may sometimes have been momentarily "caught out" — especially if you have been giving it no more than that degree of attention you habitually give to dialogue. It is because you have not followed as closely as James requires not only the completed but the uncompleted remarks, the suspended questions, the hinted inferences. (Note how James writes the kind of dialogue which comes fully to effect only when you "hear" it.)

The prose of Henry James will well repay close attention. Where a phrase may at first surprise or disconcert you, look at it again and see how precisely it renders a subtlety of definition (e.g. the opening of the second paragraph). James achieves, sometimes by a single phrase (cf. with reference to Mrs Guy the parenthesis — "she was always engaged ten parties deep") what another writer would take far longer to establish. (Collect examples which show the studied choice of adjectives and adverbs, e.g. the final sentence of *Paste*.) Perhaps Henry James will always be a writer for the few rather than for the many, although those few will be "the passionate few" (the phrase is Arnold Bennett's) by whom a classic is created. Can you, on the evidence of *Paste*, think why this partisanship over Henry James should be so acute?

2

JAMES STEPHENS

1882-1950

Novelist, considerable minor poet, short story writer. A leading figure of the Irish literary resurgence, born in the same hour and in the same city (Dublin) as James Joyce.

He came of a poor family, and grew up in the slums with hardly any formal schooling. For some years, having taught himself shorthand, he worked in an office, writing in spare-time obscurity without any sort of encouragement until "Æ" came by chance on some of his poems and stories and urged him to go on. He did, in the teeth of editorial unconcern which persisted until the appearance in 1921 of *The Crock of Gold*. At once he gained a measure of recognition and a release from drudgery; his office work went overboard and he set himself to writing as a profession, a step he never had to go back on.

Though he belonged to that international company of writers who, between the wars, made Paris almost a second home, he was in fact very much the professional Irishman. The pattern is a not uncommon blend of politics, cultural nationalism, and taproom lore: active in the Sinn Fein movement, and a worker for the establishment of the De Valera government; student of Gaelic and authority on Gaelic art; the avowed purpose (strangely echoing Joyce) of giving Ireland "a new mythology"; a great raconteur, with a vast repertory of Irish verses and stories; a singer of folk music and street ballads to concertina accompaniment. His nationalism did not prevent him from dissociating himself, as far as he could, from Ireland's neutrality in the Second World War. In a letter to *The Times* he proclaimed himself an Irishman who wished "to elect himself an Englishman for the duration". He was granted a civil pension by His Majesty's Government in 1942; though presumably not for writing to *The Times*.

Stephens was one of those writers whose work and personality are

29

very much of a piece. In the cast of his imagination no less than in appearance and behaviour, he was an original, if of a peculiarly Dublinesque kind. Less than five feet in height, with a long droll face, dark skin, and a dry smile, he had been described as looking like a leprechaun or a comic stage Irishman; and his mind moved with the lightning quickness of invention one would expect of either. "Never have I seen a man," said Burton Roscoe, "who impressed me as being so easy, free, and natural, so untamed by society, so untouched by convention, so spontaneous, pagan and joyous." These are qualities which distil themselves straight into his writing. So, for that matter, do his exuberant wit, his predilection for poverty and the underdog, and his very brogue. His friend James Joyce paid him the equivocal compliment of declaring him to be the only man capable of finishing *Finnegan's Wake* if he himself should die with that extraordinary task still unaccomplished. A more sober estimate of Stephens's work is provided by Frank Swinnerton:

> First it is a tale, and then it is philosophy, and then it is nonsense; but all these qualities are so merged and, for the reader confounded, that the effect is one of profound laughter.

The reader may of course weigh this against the present piece.

Suggested Reading: *Collected Poems* (1926); *The Crock of Gold* (1912); *Here are Ladies* (stories) (1913); *Deirdre* (1923); *Etched in Moonlight* (stories) (1928).

*　　　*　　　*

A Rhinoceros, Some Ladies, and A Horse

ONE day, in my first job, a lady fell in love with me. It was quite unreasonable, of course, for I wasn't wonderful: I was small and thin, and I weighed much the same as a largish duck-egg. I didn't fall in love with her, or anything like that. I got under the table, and stayed there until she had to go wherever she had to go to.

I had seen an advertisement — "Smart boy wanted", it said. My legs were the smartest things about me, so I went there on the run. I got the job.

At that time there was nothing on God's earth that I could do, except run. I had no brains, and I had no memory. When I was told to do anything I got into such an enthusiasm about it that I couldn't remember anything else about it. I just ran as hard as I could, and then I ran back, proud and panting. And when they asked me for the whatever-it-was that I had run for, I started, right on the instant, and ran some more.

The place I was working at was, amongst other things, a theatrical agency. I used to be sitting in a corner of the office floor, waiting to be told to run somewhere and back. A lady would come in — a music-hall lady that is — and, in about five minutes, howls of joy would start coming from the inner office. Then, peacefully enough, the lady and my two bosses would come out, and the lady always said, "Splits! I can do splits like no one". And one of my bosses would say, "I'm keeping your splits in mind." And the other would add, gallantly — "No one who ever saw your splits could ever forget 'em."

One of my bosses was thin, and the other one was fat. My fat boss was composed entirely of stomachs. He had three baby-stomachs under his chin; then he had three more descending in even larger englobings nearly to the ground: but, just before reaching the ground, the final stomach bifurcated into a pair of boots. He was very light on these and could bounce about in the neatest way.

He was the fattest thing I had ever seen, except a rhinoceros that I had met in the Zoo the Sunday before I got the job. That rhino was *very* fat, and it had a smell like twenty-five pigs. I was standing outside its palisade, wondering what it could possibly feel like to be a rhino-ceros, when two larger boys passed by. Suddenly they caught hold of me, and pushed me through the bars of the palisade. I was very skinny, and in about two seconds I was right inside, and the rhinoceros was looking at me.

It was very fat, but it wasn't fat like stomachs, it was fat like barrels of cement, and when it moved it creaked a lot, like a woman I used to know who creaked like an old bedstead. The rhinoceros swaggled over to me with a bunch of cabbage sticking out of its mouth. It wasn't angry, or anything like that, it just wanted to see who I was. Rhinos are blindish: they mainly see by smelling, and they smell in snorts. This one started at my left shoe, and snorted right up that side of me to my ear. He smelt that very carefully: then he switched over to my right ear, and snorted right down that side of me to my right shoe: then he fell in love with my shoes and began to lick them. I, naturally, wriggled my feet at that, and the big chap was so astonished that he did the strangest step-dance backwards to his pile of cabbages, and began to eat them.

I squeezed myself out of his cage and walked away. In a couple of minutes I saw the two boys. They were very frightened, and they asked me what I had done to the rhinoceros. I answered, a bit grandly, perhaps, that I had seized it in both hands, ripped it limb from limb, and tossed its carcase to the crows. But when they began shouting to people that I had just murdered a rhinoceros I took to my heels, for I didn't want to be arrested and hanged for a murder that I hadn't committed.

Still, a man can't be as fat as a rhinoceros, but my boss was as fat as a man can be. One day a great lady of the halls came in, and was received on the knee. She was very great. Her name was Maudie Darling, or thereabouts. My bosses called her nothing but "Darling", and she called them the same. When the time came for her to arrive the whole building got palpitations of the heart. After waiting a while my thin boss got angry, and said — "Who does the woman think she is? If she isn't here in two twos I'll go down to the entry, and when she does come I'll boot her out." The fat boss said — "She's only two hours late, she'll be here before the week's out."

Within a few minutes there came great clamours from the court-yard. Patriotic cheers, such as Parnell himself never got, were thundering. My bosses ran instantly to the inner office. Then the door opened, and the lady appeared.

She was very wide, and deep, and magnificent. She was dressed in camels and zebras and goats: she had two peacocks in her hat and a rabbit muff in her hand, and she strode among these with prancings.

But when she got right into the room and saw herself being looked at by three men and a boy she became adorably shy: one could see that she had never been looked at before.

"O," said she, with a smile that made three and a half hearts beat like one, "O," said she, very modestly, "is Mr Which-of-'em-is-it really in? Please tell him that Little-Miss-Me would be so glad to see and to be — "

Then the inner door opened, and the large lady was surrounded by my fat boss and my thin boss. She crooned to them — "O, you dear boys, you'll never know how much I've thought of you and longed to see you."

That remark left me stupefied. The first day I got to the office I heard that it was the fat boss's birthday, and that he was thirty years of age: and the thin boss didn't look a day younger than the fat one. How the lady could mistake these old men for boys seemed to me the strangest fact that had ever come my way. My own bet was that they'd both die of old age in about a month.

After a while they all came out again. The lady was helpless with laughter: she had to be supported by my two bosses — "O," she cried, "you boys will kill me." And the two bosses laughed and laughed, and the fat one said — "Darling, you're a scream," and the thin one said — "Darling, you're a riot."

And then ... she saw me! I saw her seeing me the very way I had seen the rhinoceros seeing me: I wondered for an instant would she smell me down one leg and up the other. She swept my two bosses right away from her, and she became a kind of queen, very glorious to behold: but sad, startled. She stretched a long, slow arm out and out and out and then she unfolded a long, slow finger, and pointed it at me — "Who is THAT?" she whispered in a strange whisper that could be heard two miles off.

My fat boss was an awful liar — "The cat brought that in," said he.

But the thin boss rebuked him: "No," he said, "it was not the cat. Let me introduce you; darling, this is James. James, this is the darling of the gods."

"And of the pit," said she, sternly.

She looked at me again. Then she sank to her knees and spread out both arms to me —

"Come to my Boozalum, angel," said she in a tender kind of way.

I knew what she meant, and I knew that she didn't know how to pronounce that word. I took a rapid glance at the area indicated. The lady had a boozalum you could graze a cow on. I didn't wait one second, but slid, in one swift, silent slide, under the table. Then she came forward and said a whole lot of poems to me under the table, imploring me, among a lot of odd things, to "come forth, and gild the morning with my eyes", but at last she was reduced to whistling at me with two fingers in her mouth, the way you whistle for a cab.

I learned after she had gone that most of the things she said to me were written by a poet fellow named Spokeshave. They were very complimentary, but I couldn't love a woman who mistook my old bosses for boys, and had a boozalum that it would take an Arab chieftain a week to trot across on a camel.

The thin boss pulled me from under the table by my leg, and said that my way was the proper way to treat a rip, but my fat boss said, very gravely — "James, when a lady invites a gentleman to her boozalum a real gentleman hops there as pronto as posssible, and I'll have none but real gentlemen in this office."

"Tell me," he went on, "what made that wad of Turkish Delight fall in love with you?"

"She didn't love me at all, sir," I answered.

"No?" he inquired.

"She was making fun of me," I explained.

"There's something in that," said he seriously, and went back to his office.

I had been expecting to be sacked that day. I was sacked the next day, but that was about a horse.

I had been given three letters to post, and told to run or they'd be too late. So I ran to the post office and round it and back, with, naturally, the three letters in my pocket. As I came to our door a nice, solid, red-faced man rode up on a horse. He thrust the reins into my hand —

"Hold the horse for a minute," said he.

"I can't," I replied, "my boss is waiting for me."

"I'll only be a minute," said he angrily, and he walked off.

Well, there was I, saddled, as it were, with a horse. I looked at it, and it looked at me. Then it blew a pint of soap-suds out of its nose and took another look at me and then the horse fell in love with me as if he had just found his long-lost foal. He started to lean against me and to

woo me with small whinneys, and I responded and replied as best I
could —

"Don't move a toe," said I to the horse, "I'll be back in a minute."

He understood exactly what I said, and the only move he made was
to swing his head and watch me as I darted up the street. I was less
than half a minute away anyhow, and never out of his sight.

Up the street there was a man, and sometimes a woman, with a
barrow, thick-piled with cabbages and oranges and apples. As I raced
round the barrow I pinched an apple off it at full speed, and in ten
seconds I was back at the horse. The good nag had watched every
move I made, and when I got back his eyes were wide open, his mouth
was wide open, and he had his legs all splayed out so that he couldn't
possibly slip. I broke the apple in halves and popped one half into his
mouth. He ate it in slow crunches, and then he looked diligently at the
other half. I gave him the other half, and, as he ate it, he gurgled with
cidery gargles of pure joy. He then swung his head round from me and
pointed his nose up the street, right at the apple-barrow.

I raced up the street again, and was back within the half-minute
with another apple. The horse had nigh finished the first half of it when
a man who had come up said, thoughtfully —

"He seems to like apples, bedad!"

"He loves them," said I.

And then, exactly at the speed of lightning, the man became angry,
and invented bristles all over himself like a porcupine —

"What the hell do you mean," he hissed, and then he bawled,
"by stealing my apples?"

I retreated a bit into the horse —

"I didn't steal your apples," I said.

"You didn't!" he roared, and then he hissed, "I saw you," he hissed.

"I didn't steal them," I explained, "I pinched them."

"Tell me that one again," said he.

"If," said I patiently, "if I took the apples for myself that would be
stealing."

"So it would," he agreed.

"But as I took them for the horse that's pinching."

"Be dam, but!" said he. "'Tis a real argument," he went on, staring
at the sky. "Answer me that one," he demanded of himself, and he

in a very stupor of intellection. "I give it up," he roared, "you give me back my apples."

I placed the half apple that was left into his hand, and he looked at it as if it was a dead frog —

"What'll I do with that?" he asked earnestly.

"Give it to the horse," said I.

The horse was now prancing at him, and mincing at him, and making love at him. He pushed the half apple into the horse's mouth, and the horse mumbled it and watched him, and chewed it and watched him, and gurgled it and watched him —

"He does like his bit of apple," said the man.

"He likes you too," said I. "I think he loves you."

"It looks like it," he agreed, for the horse was yearning at him, and its eyes were soulful.

"Let's get him another apple," said I, and, without another word, we both pounded back to his barrow and each of us pinched an apple off it. We got one apple into the horse, and were breaking the second one when a woman said gently —

"Nice, kind, Christian gentleman, feeding dumb animals — with my apples," she yelled suddenly.

The man with me jumped as if he had been hit by a train —

"Mary," said he humbly.

"Joseph," said she in a completely unloving voice.

But the woman transformed herself into nothing else but woman —

"What about my apples?" said she. "How many have we lost?"

"Three," said Joseph.

"Four," said I, "I pinched three and you pinched one."

"That's true," said he. "That's exact, Mary. I only pinched one of our apples."

"You only," she squealed —

And I, hoping to be useful, broke in —

"Joseph," said I, "is the nice lady your boss?"

He halted for a dreadful second, and made up his mind —

"You bet she's my boss," said he, "and she's better than that, for she's the very wife of my bosum."

She turned to me —

"Child of Grace — " said she —

36

Now when I was a child, and did something that a woman didn't like she always expostulated in the same way. If I tramped on her foot, or jabbed her in the stomach — the way women have multitudes of feet and stomachs is always astonishing to a child — the remark such a woman made was always the same. She would grab her toe or her stomach, and say — "Childagrace, what the hell are you doing?" After a while I worked it out that Childagrace was one word, and was my name. When any woman in agony yelled Childagrace I ran right up prepared to be punished, and the woman always said tenderly, "What are you yowling about, Childagrace."

"Childagrace," said Mary earnestly, "how's my family to live if you steal our apples? You take my livelihood away from me! Very good, but will you feed and clothe and educate my children in," she continued proudly, "the condition to which they are accustomed?"

I answered that question cautiously —

"How many kids have you, ma'am?" said I.

"We'll leave that alone for a while," she went on. "You owe me two and six for the apples."

"Mary!" said Joseph, in a pained voice.

"And you," she snarled at him, "owe me three shillings. I'll take it out of you in pints." She turned to me —

"What do you do with all the money you get from the office here?"

"I give it to my landlady."

"Does she stick to the lot of it?"

"Oh, no," I answered, "she always gives me back threepence."

"Well, you come and live with me and I'll give you back fourpence."

"All right," said I.

"By gum," said Joseph, enthusiastically, "that'll be fine. We'll go out every night and we won't steal a thing. We'll just pinch legs of beef, and pig's feet, and barrels of beer — "

"Wait now," said Mary. "You stick to your own landlady. I've trouble enough of my own. You needn't pay me the two and six."

"Good for you," said Joseph heartily, and then, to me —

"You just get a wife of your bosum half as kind as the wife of my bosum and you'll be set up for life. Mary," he cried joyfully, "let's go and have a pint on the strength of it."

"You shut up," said she.

"Joseph," I interrupted, "knows how to pronounce that word properly."

"What word?"

"The one he used when he said you were the wife of his what-you-may-call-it."

"I'm not the wife of any man's what-you-may-call-it," said she, indignantly — "Oh, I see what you mean! So he pronounced it well, did he?"

"Yes, ma'am."

She looked at me very sternly —

"How does it come you know about all these kinds of words?"

"Yes," said Joseph, and he was even sterner than she was, "when I was your age I didn't know any bad words."

"You shut up," said she, and continued, "what made you say that to me?"

"A woman came into our office yesterday, and she mispronounced it."

"What did she say now?"

"Oh, she said it all wrong."

"Do you tell me so? We're all friends here: what way did she say it, son?"

"Well, ma'am, she called it boozalum,"

"She said it wrong all right," said Joseph, "but 'tis a good, round, fat kind of word all the same."

"You shut up," said Mary. "Who did she say the word to?"

"She said it to me, ma'am."

"She must have been a rip," said Joseph.

"Was she a rip, now?"

"I don't know, ma'am. I never met a rip."

"You're too young yet," said Joseph, "but you'll meet them later on. I never met a rip myself until I got married — I mean," he added hastily, "that they were all rips except the wife of my what-do-you-call-ems, and that's why I married her."

"I expect you've got a barrel-full of rips in your past," said she bleakly, "you must tell me about some of them tonight." And then, to me, "tell us about the woman," said she.

So I told them all about her, and how she held out her arms to me, and said, "Come to my boozalum, angel."

"What did you do when she shoved out the old arms at you?" said Joseph.

"I got under the table," I answered.

"That's not a bad place at all, but," he continued earnestly, "never get under the bed when there's an old girl chasing you, for that's the worst spot you could pick on. What was the strap's name?"

"Maudie Darling, she called herself."

"You're a blooming lunatic," said Joseph, "she's the loveliest thing in the world, barring," he added hastily, "the wife of my blast-the-bloody-word."

"We saw her last night," said Mary, "at Dan Lowrey's Theatre, and she's just lovely."

"She isn't as nice as you, ma'am," I asserted.

"Do you tell me that now?" said she.

"You are twice as nice as she is, and twenty times nicer."

"There you are," said Joseph, "the very words I said to you last night."

"You shut up," said Mary scornfully, "you were trying to knock a pint out of me! Listen, son," she went on, "we'll take all that back about your landlady. You come and live with me, and I'll give you back sixpence a week out of your wages."

"All right, ma'am," I crowed in a perfectly monstrous joy.

"Mary," said Joseph, in a reluctant voice —

"You shut up," said she.

"He can't come to live with us," said Joseph. "He's a bloody Prodestan," he added sadly.

"Why — " she began —

"He'd keep me and the childer up all night, pinching apples for horses and asses, and reading the Bible, and up to every kind of devilment."

Mary made up her mind quickly —

"You stick to your own landlady," said she, "tell her that I said she

39

was to give you sixpence." She whirled about, "There won't be a thing left on that barrow," said she to Joseph.

"Damn the scrap," said Joseph violently.

"Listen," said Mary to me very earnestly, "am I nicer than Maudie Darling?"

"You are, ma'am," said I.

Mary went down on the road on her knees: she stretched out both arms to me, and said —

"Come to my boozalum, angel."

I looked at her, and I looked at Joseph, and I looked at the horse. Then I turned from them all and ran into the building and into the office. My fat boss met me —

"Here's your five bob," said he. "Get to hell out of here," said he.

And I ran out.

I went to the horse, and leaned my head against the thick end of his neck, and the horse leaned as much of himself against me as he could manage. Then the man who owned the horse came up and climbed into his saddle. He fumbled in his pocket —

"You were too long," said I. "I've been sacked for minding your horse."

"That's too bad," said he: "that's too damn bad," and he tossed me a penny.

I caught it, and lobbed it back into his lap, and I strode down the street the most outraged human being then living in the world.

COMMENTARY

Possibly some readers will be put out by the inclusion here of a story which is merely funny; and possibly some will not find this story funny. No matter. These are quite legitimate attitudes, but they do not preclude scrutiny of the story (or for that matter, of themselves). For comedy has its sources and mechanisms, and no less than any other literary kind it embodies values. As much as any other in the book, this piece merits intelligent discrimination of its qualities.

The term comedy itself is too loose to take us far. A rather pompous generalization has it that comedy is concerned with men's casual relationships as social beings, and the habits or attitudes which prompt their actions in society; but these can be treated in the most diverse ways and with various intentions. There is high comedy and there is farce, and between those poles a world of comic kinds — romantic comedy, satiric comedy, picaresque comedy, comedy of manners, of humours, of intrigue, mock heroic, burlesque, and any number of mixtures. Comedy may be the sifting of a man's moral nature, a satiric commentary on social attitudes, the poised affirmation of civilized standards; or it can propose the less sophisticated pleasure of intrigues, complications and confusions, extravagant situations and ludicrous incidents. Such differences are in great part defined by the attitudes each kind embodies or evokes: the author's attitude to his characters, to his audience, to society in general; the attitude of the characters to each other; the reader's attitude to any or all of these. And it is plainly in virtue of the values these attitudes imply that it makes sense to speak of stories as, say, trenchant or trivial, adult or naive, vital or negative, sane or sickly.

At the same time, one needs to be wary about applying normal moral standards to comedy. T. S. Eliot has put it that the essential business of the comedian is the creation of an entire comic world; and it is common experience that the world of comedy, though it has its own positive laws and values, may invite from the audience a curiously amoral response. Everyday disapproval of lying, sharking, roguery, has no place in it; one tacitly resigns the wish to censure and consents to admire, even applaud these, if they are carried through with gusto and disinterested artistry at the expense of the dull and stupid. What matters is the spirit — the vitality, the dexterity, the splendid bravura of the performance. Comedy, however little burdened with "significance", is emphatically on the side of life against poverty of spirit, of decision against timidity, of nimble witted resourcefulness against uncreative stupidity. It makes its own affirmations. (Consider in the light of what has been said the work of any comic writers you know. Some names to help the choice: Aristophanes; Plautus; Apuleius; Chaucer; Machiavelli; Rabelais; Shakespeare; Ben Jonson; Molière; Congreve; Swift; Pope; Sheridan; Voltaire; Sidney Smith; Jane Austen; Dickens; Thackeray; C. S. Calverly; Oscar Wilde; Kipling; Shaw; Leacock; Belloc; Wodehouse; Coward; Ben

Travers; Ogden Nash; any *Punch* contributor. Comparative scrutiny of popular stage comedians and comic shows might also prove interesting.)

The present story might usefully be considered under four headings: Form, Events, Manner, Attitudes. This time we need do no more than draw attention directly to some of the matters these cover.

Form. Is the story dramatic in form, or episodic? What, if anything, unifies it or holds it together? (There might of course be several things.)

Events. How important are the events of the story *in themselves?* Does any of the essential comic effect derive from these, or does it come rather from the way they are treated — the manner in which they are recounted, the attitudes adopted by the participants, etc.? (In other words, is *what* happens more important than the *way* things happen?) Do the incidents strike you as realistic? exaggerated? slight? absurd? grotesque? fantastic? picaresque?

Manner and tone. How would you characterize the language of the narration? Is there anything about it which is formal? restrained? sophisticated? elegant? urbane? mannered? Or is it nearer the tone of common speech? Could it be termed racy? low? exuberant? uninhibited? droll? flamboyant? unsophisticated? extravagant? uncouth? You will see that some or all of the suitable terms indicate that the author is assuming (for his immediate comic purpose, of course) a definite attitude towards his readers. How would you describe this attitude? Is it serious? mild? sober? responsible? confidential? impassioned? patronizing? superior? bland? gay? jaunty? cheeky? There is also the author's attitude towards his material. What element of criticism is implied in the story — is it in any way satiric, ironic, or condemnatory? Are there any judgments or evaluations at all, explicit or implied? If there are, did the author intend you to take them quite seriously? (The "viewpoint" is relevant here, of course. How does it bear on these questions that the narrator is characterized as a young boy?) What would you say of the overall air and attack of the piece — is it sober, mild, precise? Or is it irrepressibly gay and jaunty?

Attitudes. (a) What are the attitudes of the characters to each other — how do they interact and react? (Where, for example, is the comedy in the conversation between the boy, the man with the apples, and the wife?) Are they predatory? hard? cold? isolated? restrained? inhibited? bored? blasé? sophisticated? critical? cynical? Or do they rather show spontaneity, fellow-feeling, humanity, warmth, and eager interest? Could you describe these people as naive or simple in their dealings with one another? Do they perhaps blend shrewdness and naivety, simplicity and sophistication of a sort, in a kind of worldly half-wisdom? (b) How do the characters take themselves? Are they pompous? over-earnest? self-important? If they do seem to relish their own performance, is this offensive? Why not? Do you detect anywhere an element of self-mockery or self-depreciation in their attitude, a refusal to take themselves entirely seriously? (c) How do the characters face up to the events in which they are involved — or to put it more solemnly, what is their attitude to life? Do you find anything negative in this attitude? nihilistic? listless? stoic? coolly reasonable? Or is it better described as exuberant, enthusiastic, uninhibited, flamboyant, and perhaps irresponsible? You will notice that some of the most extravagant things are said and done with an air of zestful earnestness — does this mar the comedy with an out-of-place gravity? Or does it in some way flavour it? Would such characters be much put out if you found something diverting in their seriousness? What importance would you say they are likely to attach to the correctness of an action as against the spirit in which it is done, the grandiloquent panache of the gesture?

The narrator merits separate treatment. Much of the piquancy of the comedy stems from Stephens's choice of protagonist, a boy as relived by the man he becomes. This allows a kind of double focus, or running irony: the boy's innocence is set off against the man's awareness, giving a continual suggestion of tongue-in-cheek. (Can you find any places where Stephens exploits this fiction of naivety or insouciant ignorance?) But the boy himself is deftly characterized. His innocence is hardly wide-eyed or guileless — would "wary" describe it? Again, consider what the story owes to his habitual stance in the face of the people and circumstances that thrust themselves upon him. Is he emotionally involved or closely concerned? Does he appear at all impressionable, gullible, at the mercy of events or bewildered by them? Or is his incomprehension resourceful and unastonished? Would it be accurate, in all, to say that his comic attitude is a cagey detachment, an imperturbable matter-of-factness and self-possession amid a lunatic world?

"Innocence" is an elusive idea, and attempts to portray a state of innocence sometimes result in sentimentality. Why does this one not do so? Refer to other treatments of childish or adolescent innocence you know. Which of these seem to you sentimental? What makes them so? Which presentation comes nearest the truth? Use any of the following you can: the "littel scholer" in Chaucer's *Prioress' Tale*; Macduff's son; Tiny Tim, David Copperfield, Oliver Twist, Pip, Little Nell, Jo, etc.; Maggie and Tom Tulliver, in *The Mill on the Floss*: Little Lord Fauntleroy; Miles and Flora in *The Turn of the Screw*; Jim Hawkins in *Treasure Island*; the boys of Greyfriars (or any other school in fiction); William (in Richmal Crompton's "William" stories); the boy in Dylan Thomas's *Portrait of the Artist as a Young Dog*, and subsequent stories.

The last question for the reader is of course the crucial one. The story makes no claim to weight, carries no "message", displays no great reverence or seriousness. Is it, therefore, worthless?

3

JAMES JOYCE

1882-1941

With Lawrence, one of the acknowledged giants of twentieth-century literature — some would say, *the* giant. Fugitive poet; minor short story writer, with at least one masterpiece in that kind to his credit; major novelist, whose life's output of novels comes to some four works. In his life, the centre of moral and legal controversy, from which he kept aloof; since his death, the centre of literary and biographical controversy which as yet is nowhere near resolution. In almost all respects, an enigmatic figure. What no one has ever doubted is the magnitude of his native talent, and the fanaticism of his dedication.

He was one of the large family of a roistering Dublin character with little money and a good tenor voice, who was in the habit of referring to him as the favourite of his "sixteen or seventeen children". Save for the voice (Joyce's natural tenor is said to have borne comparison with the young McCormack's), Joyce appears to have taken after his artistic and sensitive mother; indeed one of the decisive actions of his life was his torment refusal to ease his mother's mind on her deathbed by acceding to her plea that he should return to the Roman Catholic Church. He was educated by the Jesuits at excellent schools — which he hated — and then at University College, Dublin, a sustained and severe intellectual discipline which plainly did much to bring his naturally subtle mind to the fantastic pitch of virtuosity he displayed, and seemed to take for granted, as a novelist. His powers declared themselves early. At nine he wrote a virulent political pamphlet, which his father had published privately; as a prize essayist he swept the board time after time; while still at University he was thanked by Ibsen, then all but unchampioned, for a paper in the *Fortnightly*

Review on *When We Dead Awaken,* which he had perforce to read in the original Norwegian, learned for the purpose. It is germane to his major work to add that Joyce was a linguist of vast range and facility, and that Norwegian was by no means the most remote of the battery of languages and dialects he knew. No less germane are the literary attitudes which gained him a certain notoriety as a young man about Dublin, and perhaps his later and wider notoriety too. He was a hunter of what he called "epiphanies", that is, rare moments of sudden and complete self-disclosure, or self-understanding. And "he said among other things that it was possible to make great art of the comedy of the mean and ordinary truth"; to which we may subjoin, with a recent *Times Literary Supplement* reviewer, indeed we know now that it was.

On taking his degree in 1902 Joyce left Dublin for Paris: "I will not serve that in which I no longer believe, whether it calls itself my home, my fatherland or my church." He had no means, was soon all but starving, and his writing was not being published. He returned in 1903, to his mother's deathbed, left home again the following year to teach elsewhere in Ireland, then still in 1904 he married and left Ireland for good, going first to Zürich and then to Trieste, where he got a job as a teacher of English in the Berlitz School at £80 a year. The rest is a history of dedicated poverty, and, for many years, complete obscurity, of a struggle for publication which has become part of literary — not to say legal — legend, and probably has no parallel anywhere in literature. What one has to remember is that it is not the casual attempt of the dilettante to win approval as a literary man, or even the old story of the hopeful who starves in a garret. Joyce, a man of immense ability, deliberately condemned himself and his family to permanent exile and hardship; he worked, not prolifically in the hope of achieving a hit and the ensuing financial reward, but as an artist, completely self-absorbed, with infinite and staggering pains, solely to realize a few brilliantly odd conceptions of esoteric appeal; and he held on in the face of blank disregard, of incomprehension and hostility, of official condemnation, and worse than any of these, of the possibility that his work was founded *in toto* on a vast mistake. Some measure of recognition followed his acceptance by the Pound-Eliot-Wyndham Lewis circle, and the *cause célèbre* of his *Ulysses,* if nothing else, made him an international figure. But despite the gifts of generous friends he never wholly escaped from financial difficulty; and his final collapse was hastened by the worry of losing almost everything in his flight before the German advance on Vichy in 1940, as well as by the poor reception of *Finnegan's Wake*.

For long troubled by failing sight which a succession of operations did little to stay, in the last ten years of his life he was almost blind, and he did his later work in a big hand on large sheets of paper. He is described as "tall, slender, very erect though loose, quiet, self-contained, courteous, almost courtly". He dressed elegantly; and he sometimes wore a black patch over his left eye, beneath the lens of his glasses. He was superstitious. Like every other Dublin writer, he set the greatest store by the street ballads and common lore of his native city, and it is only now being generally realized how intimately these permeate and shape his work.

Joyce's early volume of lyrics, *Chamber Music*, was rejected by four London publishers before it was finally accepted in 1907; and he earned nothing at all from it. *Dubliners*, completed in 1905, remained unpublished until 1914: two publishers who had accepted it earlier broke their contracts, presumably from a sudden failure of nerve, and a Dublin printer went to the length of breaking up the type after setting it rather than let Joyce buy the printed sheets to publish at his own expense. The quasi-autobiographical *Portrait of the Artist as a Young Man* was published at the instance of the Pound clique in the *Egoist*, the sheets being sent from America since, as one printer put it, "no English printer would for one moment entertain any idea of printing such a production".

These are now almost incomprehensible attitudes. The objections opposed to *Ulysses* are less so. This gigantic work, conceived in 1906 but not begun until 1914, was published finally in Paris in 1921 by the now historic enterprise of a young American bookseller named Sylvia Beach, who formed a company for the purpose. Instalments in the American *Egoist* and *Little Review* had been hotly attacked, and some of the latter burned by the U.S. Post Office for alleged obscenity, the editors suffering fines and fingerprinting; five hundred copies of the second printing of the Paris edition were burned in New York by the U.S. Post Office; all but one of the third edition of five hundred copies were confiscated at Folkestone by the Customs. The squalid business of smuggling and pirating — for in the circumstances Joyce could obtain no copyright — went on until a famous legal ruling of 1933 upheld the claim that the book was not pornography but a genuine work of art, and legalized publication in America. The first legal edition of 1934 sold 35,000 copies immediately. "Æ" described the book as the "greatest fiction of the twentieth century". Alfred Noyes is on record as declaring it 'simply the foulest book that has ever found its way into print". The *Dublin Review* lamented that "a great Jesuit-trained talent has gone over malignantly and mockingly to the powers of evil". What no one has ever called in question is the extreme virtuosity of Joyce's performance. *Ulysses* is wholly concerned with the casual events of a single day in Dublin, June 16th, 1904, rendered through the consciousness of a handful of main characters. It minutely parallels the Odyssey at every point. Each episode is written in a style appropriate to its subject; and each features some organ of the human body, a science or art, a symbol, and a colour. Keys and guides to it have been published, and they are necessary, though the book is not unintelligible without them.

Finnegan's Wake remains largely unintelligible to most readers, with or without the guides. Finished in 1939, it fully occupied Joyce for seventeen years, and is a fantastic attempt to sum up human history through the unconscious dream-world of a sleeping reveller, the language being a suitable but near-unreadable amalgam of dozens of languages including — it is said — Eskimo. It contains "not a single sentence to guide the reader in interpreting it, not a single direct statement of what it is about". All one can say of such a work now is that the verdict on it must be left to time, and the better understanding that may bring.

The way into Joyce's work for the beginner is through *Dubliners* and the *Portrait,* or perhaps better still, through the early draft of the *Portrait,* since published as *Stephen Hero.* There is little point in tackling *Ulysses* until one has learned something of Joyce and his intentions, preferably both from these earlier writings and from one or other of the books about him. *Finnegan's Wake* can be looked at.

*   *   *

A Painful Case

MR JAMES DUFFY lived in Chapelizod because he wished to live as far as possible from the city of which he was a citizen and because he found all the other suburbs of Dublin mean, modern and pretentious. He lived in an old sombre house, and from his windows he could look into the disused distillery or upwards along the shallow river on which Dublin is built. The lofty walls of his uncarpeted room were free from pictures. He had himself bought every article of furniture in the room: a black iron bedstead, an iron washstand, four cane chairs, a clothes-rack, a coal scuttle, a fender and irons and a square table on which lay a double desk. A bookcase had been made in an alcove by means of shelves of white wood. The bed was clothed with white bedclothes and a black and scarlet rug covered the foot. A little hand-mirror hung above the wash-stand and during the day a white shaded lamp stood as the sole ornament of the mantelpiece. The books on the white wooden shelves were arranged from below upwards according to bulk. A complete Wordsworth stood at one end of the lowest shelf and a copy of the *Maynooth Catechism,* sewn into the cloth cover of a note-book, stood at one end of the top shelf. Writing materials were always on the desk. In the desk lay a manuscript translation of Haupt-mann's *Michael Kramer,* the stage directions of which were written in purple ink, and a little sheaf of papers held together by a brass pin. In these sheets a sentence was inscribed from time to time and, in an ironical moment, the headline of an advertisement for *Bile Beans* had been pasted on to the first sheet. On lifting the lid of the desk a faint fragrance escaped — the fragrance of new cedar-wood pencils or of a bottle of gum or of an over ripe apple which might have been left there and forgotten.

Mr Duffy abhorred anything which betokened physical or mental disorder. A medieval doctor would have called him saturnine. His face, which carried the entire tale of his years, was of the brown tint of Dublin streets. On his long and rather large head grew dry black hair and a tawny moustache did not quite cover an unamiable mouth. His cheekbones also gave his face a harsh character; but there was no harshness in the eyes which, looking at the world from under their tawny eyebrows, gave the impression of a man ever alert to greet a

D

redeeming instinct in others but often disappointed. He lived at a little distance from his body, regarding his own acts with doubtful side-glances. He had an odd autobiographical habit which led him to compose in his mind from time to time a short sentence about himself containing a subject in the third person and a predicate in the past tense. He never gave alms to beggars, and walked firmly, carrying a stout hazel.

He had been for many years cashier of a private bank in Baggot Street. Every morning he came in from Chapelizod by tram. At midday he went to Dan Burke's and took his lunch — a bottle of lager beer and a small trayful of arrowroot biscuits. At four o'clock he was set free. He dined in an eating house in George's Street where he felt himself safe from the society of Dublin's gilded youth and where there was a certain plain honesty in the bill of fare. His evenings were spent either before his landlady's piano or roaming about the outskirts of the city. His liking for Mozart's music brought him sometimes to an opera or a concert: these were the only dissipations of his life.

He had neither companions nor friends, church nor creed. He lived his spiritual life without any communion with others, visiting his relatives at Christmas and escorting them to the cemetery when they died. He performed these two social duties for old dignity's sake, but conceded nothing further to the conventions which regulate the civic life. He allowed himself to think that in certain circumstances he would rob his bank but, as these circumstances never arose, his life rolled out evenly — an adventureless tale.

One evening he found himself sitting beside two ladies in the Rotunda. The house, thinly peopled and silent, gave distressing prophecy of failure. The lady who sat next to him looked round at the deserted house once or twice and then said:

"What a pity there is such a poor house tonight! It's so hard on people to have to sing to empty benches."

He took the remark as an invitation to talk. He was surprised that she seemed so little awkward. While they talked he tried to fix her permanently in his memory. When he learned that the young girl beside her was her daughter he judged her to be a year or so younger than himself. Her face, which must have been handsome, had remained intelligent. It was an oval face with strongly marked features. The eyes were very dark blue and steady. Their gaze began with a defiant note, but was confused by what seemed a deliberate swoon of the pupil into the iris, revealing for an instant a temperament of great sensibility. The pupil reasserted itself quickly, this half-disclosed nature fell again under the reign of prudence, and her astrakhan jacket, moulding a bosom of a certain fullness, struck the note of defiance more definitely.

He met her again a few weeks afterwards at a concert in Earlsfort Terrace and seized the moments when her daughter's attention was diverted to become intimate. She alluded once or twice to her husband, but her tone was not such as to make the allusion a warning. Her name was Mrs Sinico. Her husband's great-great-grandfather had come from Leghorn. Her husband was captain of a mercantile boat plying between Dublin and Holland; and they had one child.

Meeting her a third time by accident, he found courage to make an appointment. She came. This was the first of many meetings; they met always in the evening and chose the most quiet quarters for their walks together. Mr Duffy, however, had a distaste for underhand ways and, finding that they were compelled to meet stealthily, he forced her to ask him to her house. Captain Sinico encouraged his visits, thinking that his daughter's hand was in question. He had dismissed his wife so sincerely from his gallery of pleasures that he did not suspect that anyone else would take an interest in her. As the husband was often away and the daughter out giving music lessons, Mr Duffy had many opportunities of enjoying the lady's society. Neither he nor she had had any such adventure before and neither was conscious of any incongruity. Little by little he entangled his thoughts with hers. He lent her books, provided her with ideas, shared his intellectual life with her. She listened to all.

Sometimes in return for his theories she gave out some fact of her own life. With almost maternal solicitude she urged him to let his nature open to the full: she became his confessor. He told her that for some time he had assisted at the meetings of an Irish Socialist Party, where he had felt himself a unique figure amidst a score of sober workmen in a garret lit by an inefficient oil-lamp. When the party had divided into three sections, each under its own leader and in its own garret, he had discontinued his attendances. The workmen's discussions, he said, were too timorous; the interest they took in the question of wages was inordinate. He felt that they were hard-featured realists and that they resented an exactitude which was the produce of a leisure not within their reach. No social revolution, he told her, would be likely to strike Dublin for some centuries.

She asked him why he did not write out his thoughts. For what? he asked her, with careful scorn. To compete with phrasemongers, incapable of thinking consecutively for sixty seconds? To submit himself to the criticisms of an obtuse middle class which entrusted its morality to policemen and its fine arts to impresarios?

He went often to her little cottage outside Dublin; often they spent their evenings alone. Little by little, as their thoughts entangled, they spoke of subjects less remote. Her companionship was like a warm soil about an exotic. Many times she allowed the dark to fall upon them, refraining from lighting the lamp. The dark discreet room, their isolation, the music that still vibrated in their ears united them. This union exalted him, wore away the rough edges of his character, emotionalized his mental life. Sometimes he caught himself listening to the sound of his own voice. He thought that in her eyes he would ascend to an angelical stature; and, as he attached the fervent nature of his companion more and more closely to him, he heard the strange impersonal voice which he recognized as his own, insisting on the soul's incurable loneliness. We cannot give ourselves, it said: we are our own. The end of these discourses was that one night, during which she had shown every sign of unusual excitement, Mrs Sinico caught up his hand passionately and pressed it to her cheek.

Mr Duffy was very much surprised. Her interpretation of his words disillusioned him. He did not visit her for a week; then he wrote to her asking her to meet him. As he did not wish their last interview to be troubled by the influence of their ruined confessional they met in a little cakeshop near the Parkgate. It was cold autumn weather, but in spite of the cold they wandered up and down the roads of the Park for nearly three hours. They agreed to break off their intercourse: every bond, he said, is a bond to sorrow. When they came out of the Park they walked in silence towards the tram; but here she began to tremble so violently that, fearing another collapse on her part, he bade her goodbye quickly and left her. A few days later he received a parcel containing his books and music.

Four years passed. Mr Duffy returned to his even way of life. His room still bore witness of the orderliness of his mind. Some new pieces of music encumbered the music-stand in the lower room and on his shelves stood two volumes by Nietzsche: *Thus Spake Zarathustra* and *The Gay Science*. He wrote seldom in the sheaf of papers which lay on his desk. He kept away from concerts lest he should meet her. His father died; the junior partner of the bank retired. And still every morning he went into the city by tram and every evening walked home from the city after having dined moderately in George's Street and read the evening paper for dessert.

One evening as he was about to put a morsel of corned beef and cabbage into his mouth his hand stopped. His eyes fixed themselves on a paragraph in the evening paper which he had propped against the water-carafe. He replaced the morsel of food on his plate and read the paragraph attentively. Then he drank a glass of water, pushed his plate to one side, doubled the paper down before him between his elbows and read the paragraph over and over again. The cabbage began to deposit a cold white grease on his plate. The girl came over to him to ask was his dinner not properly cooked. He said it was very good, and ate a few mouthfuls of it with difficulty. Then he paid his bill and went out.

He walked along quickly through the November twilight, his stout hazel stick striking the ground regularly, the fringe of the buff *Mail* peeping out of a side-pocket of his tight reefer overcoat. On the lonely road which leads from the Parkgate to the Chapelizod he slackened his pace. His stick struck the ground less emphatically, and his breath, issuing irregularly, almost with a sighing sound, condensed in the wintry air. When he reached his house he went up at once to his bedroom and, taking the paper from his pocket, read the paragraph again by the failing light of the window. He read it not aloud, but moving his lips as a priest does when he reads the prayers *Secreto*. This was the paragraph:

DEATH OF A LADY AT SYDNEY PARADE
A Painful Case

Today at the City of Dublin Hospital the Deputy Coroner (in the absence of Mr Leverett) held an inquest on the body of Mrs Emily

Sinico, aged forty-three years, who was killed at Sydney Parade Station yesterday evening. The evidence showed that the deceased lady, while attempting to cross the line, was knocked down by the engine of the ten o'clock slow train from Kingstown, thereby sustaining injuries of the head and right side which led to her death.

James Lennon, driver of the engine, stated that he had been in the employment of the railway company for fifteen years. On hearing the guard's whistle he set the train in motion and a second or two afterwards brought it to rest in response to loud cries. The train was going slowly.

P. Dunne, railway porter, stated that as the train was about to start he observed a woman attempting to cross the lines. He ran towards her and shouted, but, before he could reach her, she was caught by the buffer of the engine and fell to the ground.

A juror. "You saw the lady fall?"

Witness. "Yes".

Police-Sergeant Croly deposed that when he arrived he found the deceased lying on the platform apparently dead. He had the body taken to the waiting room pending the arrival of the ambulance.

Constable 57 corroborated.

Dr Halpin, assistant house-surgeon of the City of Dublin Hospital, stated that the deceased had two lower ribs fractured and had sustained severe contusions of the right shoulder. The right side of the head had been injured in the fall. The injuries were not sufficient to have caused death in a normal person. Death, in his opinion, had been probably due to shock and sudden failure of the heart's action.

Mr H. B. Patterson Finlay, on behalf of the railway company, expressed his deep regret at the accident. The company had always taken every precaution to prevent people crossing the lines except by the bridges, both by placing notices in every station and by the use of patent spring gates at level crossings. The deceased had been in the habit of crossing the lines late at night from platform to platform and, in view of certain other circumstances of the case, he did not think the railway officials were to blame.

Captain Sinico, of Leoville, Sydney Parade, husband of the deceased also gave evidence. He stated that the deceased was his wife. He was not in Dublin at the time of the accident as he had arrived only that morning from Rotterdam. They had been married twenty-two years and had lived happily until about two years ago, when his wife began to be rather intemperate in her habits.

Miss Mary Sinico said that of late her mother had been in the habit of going out at night to buy spirits. She, witness, had often tried to reason with her mother and had induced her to join a League. She was not at home until an hour after the accident.

The jury returned a verdict in accordance with the medical evidence and exonerated Lennon from all blame.

The Deputy-Coroner said it was a most painful case, and expressed great sympathy with Captain Sinico and his daughter. He urged on the railway company to take strong measures to prevent the possibility of similar accidents in future. No blame attached to anyone.

Mr Duffy raised his eyes from the paper and gazed out of his window on the cheerless evening landscape. The river lay quiet beside the empty distillery and from time to time a light appeared in some house on the Lucan road. What an end! The whole narrative of her death revolted him and it revolted him to think that he had ever spoken to her of what he held sacred. The threadbare phrases, the inane expressions of sympathy, the cautious words of a reporter won over to conceal the details of a commonplace vulgar death attacked his stomach. Not merely had she degraded herself; she had degraded him. He saw the squalid tract of her vice, miserable and malodorous. His soul's companion! He thought of the hobbling wretches whom he had seen carrying cans and bottles to be filled by the barman. Just God, what an end! Evidently she had been unfit to live, without any strength of purpose, an easy prey to habits, one of the wrecks on which civilization has been reared. But that she could have sunk so low! Was it possible he had deceived himself so utterly about her? He remembered her outburst of that night and interpreted it in a harsher sense than he had ever done. He had no difficulty now in approving of the course he had taken.

As the light failed and his memory began to wander he thought her hand touched his. The shock which had first attacked his stomach was now attacking his nerves. He put on his overcoat and hat quickly and went out. The cold air met him on the threshold; it crept into the

sleeves of his coat. When he came to the public-house at Chapelizod
Bridge he went in and ordered a hot punch.

The proprietor served him obsequiously but did not venture to talk.
There were five or six working-men in the shop discussing the value of
a gentleman's estate in County Kildare. They drank at intervals from
their huge pint tumblers and smoked, spitting often on the floor and
sometimes dragging the sawdust over their spits with their heavy boots.
Mr Duffy sat on his stool and gazed at them without seeing or hearing
them. After a while they went out and he called for another punch.
He sat a long time over it. The shop was very quiet. The proprietor
sprawled on the counter reading the *Herald* and yawning. Now and
again a tram was heard swishing along the lonely road outside.

As he sat there, living over his life with her and evoking alternately
the two images in which he now conceived her, he realized that she was
dead, that she had ceased to exist, that she had become a memory.
He began to feel ill at ease. He asked himself what else could he have
done. He could not have carried on a comedy of deception with her;
he could not have lived with her openly. He had done what seemed to
him best. How was he to blame? Now that she was gone he understood
how lonely her life must have been, sitting night after night alone in
that room. His life would be lonely too until he, too, died, ceased to
exist, became a memory — if anyone remembered him.

It was after nine o'clock when he left the shop. The night was cold
and gloomy. He entered the Park by the first gate and walked along
under the gaunt trees. He walked through the bleak alleys where they
had walked four years before. She seemed to be near him in the
darkness. At moments he seemed to feel her voice touch his ear, her
hand touch his. He stood still to listen. Why had he withheld life
from her? Why had he sentenced her to death? He felt his moral
nature falling to pieces.

When he gained the crest of the Magazine Hill he halted and looked
along the river towards Dublin, the lights of which burned redly and
hospitably in the cold night. He looked down the slope and, at the
base, in the shadow of the wall of the Park, he saw some human
figures lying. Those venal and furtive loves filled him with despair.
He gnawed the rectitude of his life; he felt that he had been outcast
from life's feast. One human being had seemed to love him and he had

denied her life and happiness: he had sentenced her to ignominy, a death of shame. He knew that the prostrate creatures down by the wall were watching him and wishing him gone. No one wanted him, he was outcast from life's feast. He turned his eyes to the grey gleaming river winding along towards Dublin. Beyond the river he saw a goods train winding out of Kingsbridge station, like a worm with a fiery head winding through the darkness, obstinately and laboriously. It passed slowly out of sight; but still he heard in his ears the laborious drone of the engine reiterating the syllables of her name.

He turned back the way he had come, the rhythm of the engine pounding in his ears. He began to doubt the reality of what memory told him. He halted under a tree and allowed the rhythm to die away. He could not feel her near him in the darkness nor her voice touch his ear. He waited for some minutes listening. He could hear nothing: the night was perfectly silent. He listened again: perfectly silent. He felt that he was alone.

COMMENTARY

The coroner's tag Joyce uses as his title may seem all too evidently apt for a piece about a banal little affair of the suburbs, depressing in its shabby futility. True there is a plot of sorts, turning on the old romantic axis of love and death. But romantic is the last word one would use for it. The participants are middle-aged and low-spirited, if not positively cheerless; the affair breaks off with the first small hint of feeling; the death is desultory and squalid, not less so in effect because it is reported with the dreary literalness of the inquest-hack. Moreover, as if this were not dismal enough, Joyce seems to have cultivated something of the hack's literalness himself. He is at pains to fix a situation in all its tedious particularity, registering the trivia with photographic detachment simply (as it appears) because they are there, a meticulous care which he also extends to his Dublin topography. Towards his characters he maintains a like neutrality; he sets himself to record, not to participate, and what warmth their stir engenders is theirs not his. Yet meagre as it all sounds, probably even a first reading is enough to satisfy a responsive reader that this is work of quite unusual seriousness, and in its way, of quite unusual beauty.

One could fairly allow the corollary that it is wrought with unusual care. Whatever the appearance of aimlessness there is nothing random about the way the piece is put together; on the contrary, it is characterized by a spare symmetry, a highly conscious and sensitive control of artifice, an undeviating purity of intention. The plain evidence that Joyce knew just what he was after and had minutely calculated the means of getting it is his steadiness of focus — not in any case an obvious focus with this material. It is, in a strict sense, Duffy's story: everthing in it, including the literal detail and Mrs Sinico herself, is referred to him, and to one crucial element of his nature. From him again the narrative gets its shape. The pattern of the plot exactly traces the pattern of his inner drama; its fluctuations, unspectacular as they appear, are nothing less than the peaks and shallows of his whole moral existence. To plot this graph is to see the neat economy, as well as the symmetry, of Joyce's scheme. He attempts to catch the essential truth of a man's life by seizing on its two critical moments, which he presents as climaxes, counterpoised as it were on either side of the dull level of routine existence; or to find a figure more appropriate to the flux of the emotions, a crescendo, abruptly arrested, offsets a slow diminuendo, a dwindling to a single irreducible point of desolation. More remarkable, but completely characteristic, is the subtle rhetoric with which Joyce orchestrates Duffy's emotional career. Its quiet modulations attest an artistry painstaking to a fault in its attention to nuance of phrase, sentence-structure, and syntax, and an exquisite sensitivity to the emotional overtones of these.

Of course, this only raises more acutely the question whether Duffy is worth it. What is his drama, after all? Evidently it is nothing so external as frustrated love; nor is it in the last resort a dilemma of moral responsibility or guilt, though that is certainly part of it. What Joyce essays, it seems, is something more inward still, and more central to the general condition of human nature. In Ibsenite phraseology, he offers us a drama of the inner life, and its crux is the classic issue of wilful choice and self-blindness.

One might approach Joyce's intention through his solution of the technical problem he sets himself, which is that of conveying thus briefly, and with only the flimsiest action, that close understanding of his protagonist without which the story would be unintelligible.

His method of doing this is typically oblique; though again reminiscent of Ibsen. One might call it behaviourist: the character is built up from the outside, by the enumeration of a great many small facts about him which the reader is called upon to interpret. (Does this appear to you a more "natural" or fair method than the usual one, in which the author assumes inside knowledge? What advantages and disadvantages might ensue from this seeming withdrawal of the author?) We are to infer Duffy's nature and condition from the evidence of his physical, intellectual, and moral habits which we find in his room, his daily routine, his recreation, his consciousness, and more important, from the slow inner impoverishment these witness (what evidence of such impoverishment can you find?) Joyce has only to present this stituation for the reader to feel the irony of its solitary futility; but the deeper irony is that Duffy himself is not consciously aware of his meagreness at all. Nor does the affair with Mrs Sinico bring this home to him. Indeed, the marrow of the matter there is his blindness to what is staring him in the face, his complete unconsciousness of the emotional need which he is even then seeking to satisfy. (Why does Joyce make the offending gesture such a tiny one?) Hence, although he is offered a kind of salvation, and responds to the offer, he deliberately forfeits it because he mistakes the nature of that response, and himself. (Joyce makes no overt comment on Duffy's talk of politics and ideas: how seriously is one to take it? Is it as important to Mrs Sinico as it is to him? What is its real importance to her?)

What really tells against Duffy of course is his mechanical — if not quite complacent — resumption of his former sterile regimen, and even more, his first self-righteous reaction to the report of Mrs Sinico's death. (His fastidiousness is well-established before that example of it which breaks off the relationship: what is the real irony, for him, in the manner of Mrs Sinico's death and of his hearing of it? Why is this a particularly searching irony, and where does Joyce indicate its full impact on him? What is Mrs Sinico's tragedy? Does the squalidity of her death make it more poignant, or less?) This surface complacency it is the function of the inquest-report to shatter, and the climax thus precipitated is a crisis of Duffy's whole being just because he cannot now evade reality: his values, and his life, are cruelly sifted by their outcome. He is forced, reluctantly and painfully, to a recognition, that classical *anagnorisis*, or "moment of truth", which is an earnest of high seriousness in drama; and like the tragic hero he reaches his reality through a stripping bare of all less fundamental matters, a disintegration of the pretensions and self-delusions which had impeded his understanding. Simply, he comes to see himself. It is this process which is enacted in that long exquisitely modulated final section, the grave intensity of whose culmination is surpassed by the last page of *The Dead* but not much else. Here the drab, the squalid, and the humdrum are transcended, not because they can be avoided or ignored, but because they are never more than clogs to the vision of that interior truth which is Joyce's concern. And this is an austere truth; for it may be that in the last resort a dilemma like Duffy's is anyway inescapable — "We cannot give ourselves ... we are our own."

The idea for the story might well have come to Joyce from some such local press-report as he gives: what would be the straightforward way of handling that material? Given some distribution of interest between the man and the woman, what sort of story would emerge? What might a writer be after in essaying it? What does Joyce forgo in concentrating so relentlessly on Duffy? Given the decision to write the story round the man, how might a writer less clear about his intentions have dissipated or blurred his effect? "A married woman is denied emotional outlet, now that Chapelizod, Chapelle d'Iseult, no longer stands for romance" (L. A. G. Strong, *The Sacred River*, p.22). This is part of the story: is it the important part? Does it seem in itself promising material for a story?

How is Joyce's purpose furthered by the fact that his story centres on the humdrum lives of ordinary people? Would not quite exceptional spirits — like the characters of tragedy — have served his turn better?

Why is the mood of the piece finally lyric, rather than harsh or harrowing or pathetic?

Does the story gain anything by its intimate Dublin setting? Would you say, for example, that Joyce achieves an especially close integration between the topography of the city and the mechanics of the action? Or more striking, does he anywhere manage to use particular local features actually to further or enrich his communication?

Trace the stages of Duffy's self-realization after his reading the inquest-report: do his movements underline or assist this development? For what purposes does Joyce employ his technique of naturalistic detail in this part of the story? Do you find any special subtlety, perhaps ironic, in the detail of the last Ibsen-like scene on the hill — the lights, the "prostrate creatures", the train? What part in building the whole climax is played by the following: imagery; repetition; syntax (look, for example, at the concluding paragraph); variation of sentence-length; phrasing and cadence? How would you require a reader to deliver the last three or four paragraphs: in the flat and prosaic manner of the early part of the story? conversationally? in a declamatory style? very dramatically or urgently? Or would a kind of austere but exalted intonation better catch the mood?

How would you characterize Joyce's manner throughout the story: urgent? dramatic? warm and forceful? cold and nerveless? affected or precious? austere? meticulous? dry? spare? flowery?

4

CARADOC EVANS

1883-1945

PATRIARCH, in his day, of the Anglo-Welsh school of writers, and like many of his protégés a specialist in the short story form. A legend-laden name, still apt to fire rare fury in some parts of Wales.

He came of peasant stock, and grew to young manhood in the Calvinist farming community of Cardiganshire which later afforded most of his material. The youngest but one of the five children of an auctioneer and estate agent, his prospects were all but irremediably blighted when his father died at thirty, leaving the family in poverty. His formal education never went beyond the elementary skills imparted at the free board school. "Next to the preacher the schoolmaster was the worst tyrant in the place. He also was religious. He taught me a little penmanship and a little English reading, but I never had the ghost of an idea what I was reading."

A profession was out of the question. At fourteen he was apprenticed to a draper in Carmarthen. "It was at this draper's shop that I first tasted fresh meat. My stumbling block was the English language. I used to make customers laugh by my misuse of words." From Carmarthen he went to Cardiff — "slavery ... We slept eight in a room and were badly fed." He moved to London, "and was sacked from one job after another for my incompetence". In an effort to take up journalism he attended classes at the Working Men's College in Camden Town, but "I couldn't make progress in English". He lost his twelfth job in London and vowed never to return to shop work:

One morning I put on my frock coat and silk hat, which was the draper's uniform, and walked into the office of a small weekly publication. The editor-proprietor engaged me; four weeks later he tried to borrow ten pounds. When I said I didn't have it, he replied, "Good God, if I hadn't thought you a rich fellow, I wouldn't have engaged you."

None the less he was now set on a literary career:

I wanted to write stories, but I did not know what to write about. Then one night I opened the Bible and said to myself, "This is the way to learn English." I said further, "Why not try to write a Welsh story in Biblical English?" I have been trying to do that ever since.

His first volume of stories, *My People,* at once drew the attention of critics and the wrath of his people. It also aroused some bewilderment among his early acquaintances. "My uncle, whose memory I hate, noised it about that he had had me educated ... but the village schoolmaster said, 'If Caradoc can write a book the village idiot can write a new Bible.' "

He established himself in journalism, and worked subsequently on the editorial staffs of a number of periodicals, including *Cassell's Weekly* and *Everybody's Weekly.*

Evans's writing shows an almost obsessive preoccupation with one theme: the squalor of that special kind of human frailty which *in his eyes* (a necessary qualification) governed his native Cardiganshire community, a compound of religious tyranny, miserliness amounting to dishonesty, and canting hypocrisy. Naomi Royde-Smith called him "the greatest satirist of his own people since Swift", but despite the obvious affinity in tone and method a more illuminating comparison might be with Pope. It is a question whether the sardonic savagery of his arraignment is an anguished expression of final disgust, or just embittered rancour, calculated to wound and shock; nor can one discount his grim pleasure in baring what Gwyn Jones well called the "twisted souls and foxy minds of ... spiritual troglodytes". At all events, he aimed to provoke, and he succeeded. His sincerity and veracity were alike hotly called in question; his books were banned, even publicly burned; at least one of his lectures started a riot; he was verbally assailed and physically menaced; Lloyd George denounced him as a renegade. In his own words, "The repute of the man who

63

defrauds servant girls with coloured bibles was fairer in Wales than mine." All this he throve on. The more violent the assault, the more vehement his defiance. "I told the truth. And it was the stinking truth."

The centre of tumult, he shunned society and led a quiet life. One of his few intimates described him thus, a few years before his death:

> a lean figure, dark of hair and visage, and heavily lined. He has the smouldering gloom of his race that flashes now and then into nervous heat. Never yet has he been known to keep an appointment. He talks in cascades, words tumbling over each other, precisely opposite to the caustic manner of his work. He likes plain company, pipes, old taverns, and beer.

He wrote one play, and was active backstage in the repertory theatre run at Aberystwyth by his wife (the popular novelist Oliver Sandys). His death brought a flood of tributes from people who had known him personally, in Aberystwyth and elsewhere.

Suggested Reading: *My People* (1915); *Capel Sion* (1916); *Nothing to Pay* (1930); *This Way to Heaven* (1933); *Wasps* (1934); *Pilgrims in a Foreign Land* (1942); *Earth Gives All and Takes All* (1947).

*   *   *

Be This Her Memorial

MICE and rats, as it is said, frequent neither churches nor poor men's homes. The story I have to tell you about Nanni — the Nanni who was hustled on her way to prayer-meeting by the Bad Man, who saw the phantom mourners bearing away Twm Tybach's coffin, who saw the Spirit Hounds and heard their moanings two days before Isaac Penparc took wing — the story I have to tell you contradicts that theory.

Nanni was religious; and she was old. No one knew how old she was, for she said that she remembered the birth of each person that gathered in Capel Sion; she was so old that her age had ceased to concern.

She lived in the mud-walled, straw-thatched cottage on the steep road which goes up from the Garden of Eden, and ends at the tramping way that takes you into Cardigan town; if you happen to be travelling that way you may still see the roofless walls which were silent witnesses to Nanni's great sacrifice — a sacrifice surely counted unto her for righteousness, though in her search for God she fell down and worshipped at the feet of a god.

Nanni's income was three shillings and ninepence a week. That sum was allowed her by Abel Shones, the officer for Poor Relief, who each pay-day never forgot to remind the crooked, wrinkled, toothless old woman how much she owed to him and God.

"If it was not for me, little Nanni," Abel was in the habit of telling her, "you would be in the House of the Poor long ago."

At that remark Nanni would shiver and tremble.

"Dear heart," she would say in the third person, for Abel was a mighty man and the holder of a proud office, "I pray for him night and day."

Nanni spoke the truth, for she did remember Abel in her prayers. But the workhouse held for her none of the terrors it holds for her poverty stricken sisters. Life was life anywhere, in cottage or in poorhouse, though with this difference: her liberty in the poorhouse would be so curtailed that no more would she be able to listen to the spirit-laden eloquence of the Respected Josiah Bryn-Bevan. She helped to bring Josiah into the world; she swaddled him in her own flannel petticoat; she watched him going to and coming from school; she knitted for him four pairs of strong stockings to mark his going out into the world as a farm servant; and when the boy, having obeyed the command of the Big Man, was called to minister to the congregation of Capel Sion, even Josiah's mother was not more vain than Old Nanni. Hence Nanni struggled on less than three shillings and ninepence a week, for did she not give a tenth of her income to the treasury of the Capel? Unconsciously she came to regard Josiah as greater than God: God was abstract; Josiah was real.

As Josiah played a part in Nanni's life, so did a Seller of Bibles play a minor part in the last few days of her travail. The man came to Nanni's cottage the evening of the day of the rumour that the Respected Josiah Bryn-Bevan had received a call from a wealthy sister church in

Aberystwyth. Broken with grief, Nanni, the first time for many years, bent her stiffened limbs and addressed herself to the living God.

"Dear little Big Man," she prayed, "let not your son bach religious depart."

Then she recalled how good God had been to her, how He had permitted her to listen to His son's voice; and another fear struck her heart.

"Dear little Big Man," she muttered between her blackened gums, "do you now let me live to hear the boy's farewell words."

At that moment the Seller of Bibles raised the latch of the door.

"The Big Man be with this household," he said, placing his pack on Nanni's bed.

"Sit you down," said Nanni "and rest yourself, for you must be weary."

"Man," replied the Seller of Bibles, "is never weary of well-doing."

Nanni dusted for him a chair.

"No, no; indeed now," he said; "I cannot tarry long, woman. Do you not know that I am the Big Man's messenger? Am I not honoured to take His word into the highways and byways, and has He not sent me here?"

He unstrapped his pack, and showed Nanni a gaudy volume with a clasp of brass, and containing many coloured prints; the pictures he explained at hazard: here was a tall-hatted John baptizing, here a Roman-featured Christ praying in the Garden of Gethsemane, here a frock-coated Moses and the Tablets.

"A Book," said he, "which ought to be on the table of every Christian home."

"Truth you speak, little man," remarked Nanni. "What shall I say you are asking for it?"

"It has a price far above rubies," answered the Seller of Bibles. He turned over the leaves and read: " 'The labourer is worthy of his hire.' Thus it is written. I will let you have one copy — one copy only — at cost price."

"How good you are, dear me!" exclaimed Nanni.

"This I can do," said the Seller of Bibles, "because my Master is the Big Man."

"Speak you now what the cost price is."

"A little sovereign, that is all."

"Dear, dear; the Word of the little Big Man for a sovereign!"

"Keep you the Book on your parlour table for a week. Maybe others who are thirsty will see it."

Then the Seller of Bibles sang a prayer; and he departed.

Before the week was over the Respected Josiah Bryn-Bevan announced from his pulpit that in the call he had discerned the voice of God bidding him go forth into the vineyard.

Nanni went home and prayed to the merciful God: "Dear little Big Man, spare me to listen to the farewell sermon of your saint."

Nanni informed the Seller of Bibles that she would buy the Book, and she asked him to take it away with him and have written inside it an inscription to the effect that it was a gift from the least worthy of his flock to the Respected Josiah Bryn-Bevan, D.D., and she requested him to bring it back to her on the eve of the minister's farewell sermon.

She then hammered hobnails into the soles of her boots, so as to render them more durable for tramping to such capels as Bryn-Bevan happened to be preaching in. Her absences from home became a byword, occurring as they did in the haymaking season. Her labour was wanted in the fields. It was the property of the community, the community which paid her three shillings and ninepence a week.

One night Sadrach Danyrefail called at her cottage to commandeer her services for the next day. His crop had been on the ground for a fortnight, and now that there was a prospect of fair weather he was anxious to gather it in. Sadrach was going to say hard things to Nanni, but the appearance of the gleaming-eyed creature that drew back the bolts of the door frightened him and tied his tongue. He was glad that the old woman did not invite him inside, for from within there issued an abominable smell such as might have come from the boiler of the witch who at one time lived on the moor. In the morning he saw Nanni trudging towards a distant capel where the Respected Josiah Bryn-Bevan was delivering a sermon in the evening. She looked less bent and not so shrivelled up as she did the night before. Clearly, sleep had given her fresh vitality.

Two Sabbaths before the farewell sermon was to be preached Nanni came to Capel Sion with an ugly sore at the side of her mouth; repulsive matter oozed slowly from it, forming into a head, and then coursing thickly down her chin on to the shoulder of her black cape, where it glistened among the beads. On occasions her lips tightened, and she swished a hand angrily across her face.

"Old Nanni," folk remarked while discussing her over their dinner-tables, "is getting as dirty as an old sow."

During the week two more sores appeared; the next Sabbath Nanni had a strip of calico drawn over her face.

Early on the eve of the farewell Sabbath the Seller of Bibles arrived with the Book, and Nanni gave him a sovereign in small money. She packed it up reverently, and betook herself to Sadrach Danyrefail to ask him to make the presentation.

At the end of his sermon the Respected Josiah Bryn-Bevan made reference to the giver of the Bible, and grieved that she was not in the Capel. He dwelt on her sacrifice. Here was a Book to be treasured, and he could think of no one who would treasure it better than Sadrach Danyrefail, to whom he would hand it in recognition of his work in the School of the Sabbath.

In the morning the Respected Josiah Bryn-Bevan, making a tour of his congregation, bethought himself of Nanni. The thought came to him on leaving Danyrefail, the distance betwixt which and Nanni's cottage is two fields. He opened the door and called out:

"Nanni."

None answered.

He entered the room. Nanni was on the floor.

"Nanni, Nanni!" he said. "Why for you do not reply to me? Am I not your shepherd?"

There was no movement from Nanni. Mishtir Bryn-Bevan went on his knees and peered at her. Her hands were clasped tightly together, as though guarding some great treasure. The minister raised himself and prised them apart with the ferrule of his walking-stick. A roasted rat revealed itself. Mishtir Bryn-Bevan stood for several moments spellbound and silent; and in the stillness the rats crept boldly out of their hiding places and resumed their attack on Nanni's face. The minister, startled and horrified, fled from the house of sacrifice.

COMMENTARY

What strikes one at once about this story is its grim force. It shocks, and it is intended to shock. No doubt the immediate reason for its impact is the sheer loathsomeness of the account of Nanni's decline and death, but in point of fact the two climactic scenes do no more than concentrate in physical detail a mood which drives through the whole piece, and the author would quite certainly have maintained that his nauseating description only speaks of something still more nauseating. The outstanding technical feature of the story is that Evans does not tell us explicitly what that is. He leaves the reader to infer it from the manner and tone of his narration, and from his arrangement of the events. In other words, here is a case where the author's intention can be approached through his technique. (Compare the deliberate exploitation of the shock of physical horror in this story with other examples you have met — for example, in Poe, Swift, Sophocles, Shakespeare, Shelley, Spillane, etc. What is the author's purpose in each case? One characteristic of melodrama is its dabbling in horrors for their own sake — the product, usually, of a morbid or disingenuous wish to exploit the reader's sadistic impulses. Which of your examples tend towards melodrama? Would you accept "morbid" as an accurate description of Caradoc Evans's story?)

Evans's narrative manner contrasts arrestingly with that of some other authors represented in this book (compare Henry James or Joyce). This piece is distinguished by its extreme economy. It is spare, terse, concentrated. You might consider what is gained by the stark brevity of its few scenes, and the fact that they are almost all played out in the same bare room. There is no attempt at verbal evocation, scene-painting, or overt analysis of character. The few descriptions are bleak, devoid of obvious artifice; the impression produced is that of a cold recording of facts, as though the situation were being allowed to make its own solid impact. Nor is there any apparent engineering or preparation of effects. They are just suddenly and horribly *there*, as startling to the reader as to the participant. (Consider the handling of one or two of these scenes — for example, Sadrach's visit, or Nanni's last appearance in chapel, or the "house of sacrifice". Would Evans have gained if he had not been content just to list the revolting details in a blunt matter-of-fact way, without comment, but had worked up the scene in subtle profusion of description and with open display of feeling? What in short is the effect of his matter-of-factness, his seeming lack of artifice, his earthy tangibility? Compare Dickens's approach — for example, in Jo's deathbed scene in *Bleak House*. One mark of sentimentality is an indulgence in emotion for its own sake. Which author's approach brings him nearer sentimentality?)

With Evans's starkness of manner goes a sinewy brusqueness of style, a stern lucidity, showing itself through short phrases and cadences, simplicity of diction, and a kind of luminous homeliness in the trick of speech. (What impression of the author's motive in recounting the tale is the reader likely to receive from his air of blunt simplicity?) There is a total eschewal of the rhetorical, the elegant, the evocative, as of any apparent subtlety or complexity of style. What artifice there is does not obtrude; one is conscious of natural muscle, not cultivated grace. Yet the writing is markedly individual. The turn of phrase is distinctive; the rhythm and balance of the sentence are arresting; the diction, if plain, is ever-so-slightly unusual. (You might find and analyse examples of these and other individual traits.) There is a telling use of what one might call the lapidary finality, the short pregnant phrase which seems to leave nothing more to be said — "She was so old that her age had ceased to concern." (Do you find anything to account for the impression of rugged strength Evans's writing gives, in his obvious affinity with the environment he treats in this story? Does his very unliterary style, for one thing, perhaps show one dominant literary influence, inevitable in that environment?)

None the less the piece is plainly not cool objective reporting; and its overall force is more than the wash of a thrusting personality. Consider the pattern of the events. The bible-seller mouths moral platitudes while he smugly exploits the simple old pauper with shoddy sales-talk and a shoddier product. The community, through Shones, unceasingly reminds Nanni that she is kept alive by its charity; and it has no atom of concern for her beyond the work it can squeeze out of her. Bryn-Bevan's self-advertising and self-righteous unction does not disguise his real motive for changing churches, or conceal the relief with which he thrusts the pitiful symbol of the old woman's grim sacrifice on to the wealthiest man in the parish. Each instance turns on the ironic contrast between what is professed and what is actually felt or done — on hypocrisy, in a word. And then one might sift the implications further. What is Nanni's motive in praying for Jones, and in her devotion to Bryn-Bevan? And what is the dominant motive of every other character in the story? Yet it is the Bryn-Bevans and the Danyrefails of this world who gain success and esteem as the pillars of their community, and the Nannis who are exploited and despised. Again, what is the effect of the last four words? Does that description answer ironically to anything in the first sentence? (Is Evans perhaps suggesting something about the nature of the true Church as against the false, Nanni as against Bryn-Bevan?) What, finally, is the import of the title? (You might make a list of all the ironies you can find in the story. Its length may surprise you.)

This then is the crux of the story. It is a sifting of moral values; and its instrument is irony. The starkness, the force, the horror, even the apparent detachment, are expressions of the same mood and accessories to the same ends. The mood is indignation. The ends are the coldly ferocious exposure of hypocrisy and the bitter arraignment of the judgments of this world. (Evans's attitude might justly be termed pessimistic. Would "cynical" also be appropriate? Why might it not be? Do you find any similarities between this story and the work of, say, Ben Jonson, Swift, Ibsen, Samuel Butler, George Orwell, Angus Wilson? What ends, and what means, might these have in common?)

5

D. H. LAWRENCE

1885-1930

It is given to few to produce an effect on their generation such as Lawrence had. Both by his personality and by his writing — writing that was always the direct and immediate expression of himself — Lawrence was felt as a prophet, as one who declares by his life as by his words a revelation of truth. Lawrence stood for a way of life. And that way was a challenge to the whole prevailing ethos of his time. In an age of science he declared: "All scientists are liars. Liars. Liars"; in a society of traditional bourgeois values he refused to live or write in a conformist manner; in a world that cheapened and exploited sex he preached the essential sanctity of sex. Of course he was misunderstood and even prosecuted, but he never yielded. It is indeed possible to argue that Lawrence's creed was mistaken, impracticable and wholly unrealistic; that Lawrence held it with passionate conviction and expressed it in some of the finest prose and verse of our time is undeniable.

D. H. Lawrence was born in 1885 in Eastwood, "a mining village [so he describes it] of some three thousand souls, about eight miles from Nottingham, and one mile from the small stream, the Erewash, which divides Nottinghamshire from Derbyshire". He was the son of a miner and a woman of some refinement whose possessiveness had much influence in his development. After local schooling and further education at Nottingham High School and Nottingham University College Lawrence became a teacher in Croydon, but (as his poems of the period tell) he was out of his element there, and he resolved to break away and live by writing.

In 1912 he met Frieda, a German woman of aristocratic descent, and at once formed with her a union that lasted throughout his life. They had many difficulties to overcome — she was a married woman with two children, she came under ignorant suspicion when the 1914 war broke out, they were short of money, his health was uncertain — but they prevailed because of their love. When the war was over, Lawrence and his wife travelled restlessly all over the world — ever seeking a place not so much of escape as of fulfilment — but not in Italy or France, Australia or Mexico, could Lawrence find peace. His health, always threatened by tuberculosis, weakened and he died in the south of France in 1930.

As a writer Lawrence must first be remembered for his integrity. Whether as poet, novelist or short story writer, he would write only as his spirit moved him. What he was primarily concerned about is revealed in this comment of his on the novel: "It is the way our sympathy flows and recoils that really determines our lives ... for it is in the *passional* secret places of life, above all, that the tide of sensitive awareness needs to ebb and flow, cleansing and freshening." And what he felt about conventional form is made clear in this: "They want me to have form: that means they want me to have *their* pernicious, ossiferous, skin-and-grief form, and I won't." No one has written more realistically and at the same time more sensitively of the working class than Lawrence. Something of that distinctive achievement is to be found in *Tickets, Please*.

Suggested Reading: *The White Peacock* (1911); *Sons and Lovers* (1913); *The Rainbow* (1915); *Letters* ed. Aldous Huxley; *Collected Poems*.

*   *   *

Tickets, Please

THERE is in the Midlands a single-line tramway system which boldly leaves the county town and plunges off into the black, industrial countryside, up hill and down dale, through the long ugly villages of workmen's houses, over canals and railways, past churches perched high and nobly over the smoke and shadows, through stark, grimy, cold little market-places, tilting away in a rush past cinemas and shops down to the hollow where the collieries are, then up again, past a little rural church, under the ash trees, on in a rush to the terminus, the last little ugly place of industry, the cold little town that shivers on the edge of the wild, gloomy country beyond. There the green and creamy coloured tram-car seems to pause and purr with curious satisfaction. But in a few minutes — the clock on the turret of the Co-operative Wholesale Society's shops gives the time — away it starts once more on the adventure. Again there are the reckless swoops down hill, bouncing the loops: again the chilly wait in the hill-top market-place: again the breathless slithering round the precipitous drop under the church: again the patient halts at the loops, waiting for the out-coming car: so on and so on, for two long hours, till at last the city looms beyond the fat gas-works, the narrow factories draw near, we are in the sordid streets of the great town, once more we sidle to a standstill at our terminus, abashed by the great crimson and cream-coloured city cars, but still perky, jaunty, somewhat dare-devil, green as a jaunty sprig of parsley out of a black colliery garden.

To ride on these cars is always an adventure. Since we are in wartime, the drivers are men unfit for active service: cripples and hunchbacks. So they have the spirit of the devil in them. The ride becomes a steeplechase. Hurray! we have leapt in a clear jump over the canal bridge — now for the four-lane corner. With a shriek and a trail of sparks we are clear again. To be sure, a tram often leaps the rails — but what matter! It sits in a ditch till other trams come to haul it out. It is quite common for a car, packed with one solid mass of living people, to come to a dead halt in the midst of unbroken blackness, the heart of nowhere on a dark night, and for the driver and the girl conductor to call: "All get off — the car's on fire!" Instead, however, of rushing out in a panic, the passengers stolidly reply: "Get on — get on! We're not coming out. We're stopping where we are. Push on, George." So till flames actually appear.

The reason for this reluctance to dismount is that the nights are howlingly cold, black, and windswept, and a car is a haven of refuge. From village to village the miners travel, for a change of cinema, of girl, of pub. The trams are desperately packed. Who is going to risk himself in the black gulf outside, to wait perhaps an hour for another tram, then to see the forlorn notice "Depot Only", because there is something wrong! Or to greet a unit of three bright cars all so tight with people that they sail past with a howl of derision. Trams that pass in the night.

This, the most dangerous tram-service in England, as the authorities themselves declare, with pride, is entirely conducted by girls, and driven by rash young men, a little crippled, or by delicate young men, who creep forward in terror. The girls are fearless young hussies. In their ugly blue uniform, skirts up to their knees, shapeless old peaked caps on their heads, they have all the *sang-froid* of an old non-commissioned officer. With a tram packed with howling colliers, roaring hymns downstairs and a sort of antiphony of obscenities upstairs, the lasses are perfectly at their ease. They pounce on the youths who try to evade their ticket-machine. They push off the men at the end of their distance. They are not going to be done in the eye — not they. They fear nobody — and everybody fears them.

"Hello, Annie!"

"Hello, Ted!"

"Oh, mind my corn, Miss Stone. It's my belief you've got a heart of stone, for you've trod on it again."

"You should keep it in your pocket," replies Miss Stone, and she goes sturdily upstairs in her high boots.

"Tickets, please."

She is peremptory, suspicious, and ready to hit first. She can hold her own against ten thousand. The step of that tram-car is her Thermopylae.

Therefore, there is a certain wild romance aboard these cars — and in the sturdy bosom of Annie herself. The time for soft romance is in the morning, between ten o'clock and one, when things are slack: that is, except market-day and Saturday. Thus Annie has time to look about her. Then she often hops off her car and into a shop where she has spied something, while the driver chats in the main road. There is very good feeling between the girls and the drivers. Are they not companions in peril, shipments aboard this careering vessel of a tram-car, for ever rocking on the waves of a stormy land.

Then, also, during the easy hours, the inspectors are most in evidence. For some reason, everybody employed in this tram-service is young: there are no grey heads. It would not do. Therefore the inspectors are of the right age, and one, the chief, is also good-looking. See him stand on a wet, gloomy morning, in his long oilskin, his peaked cap well down over his eyes, waiting to board a car. His face is ruddy, his small brown moustache is weathered, he has a faint impudent smile. Fairly tall and agile, even in his waterproof, he springs aboard a car and greets Annie.

"Hello, Annie! Keeping the wet out?"

"Trying to."

There are only two people in the car. Inspecting is soon over. Then for a long and impudent chat on the footboard, a good easy, twelve-mile chat.

The inspector's name is John Thomas Raynor — always called John Thomas, except sometimes, in malice, Coddy. His face sets in fury when he is addressed, from a distance, with this abbreviation. There is considerable scandal about John Thomas in half a dozen villages. He flirts with the girl conductors in the morning, and walks out with them in the dark night, when they leave their tram-car at the depot. Of course, the girls quit the service frequently. Then he flirts and walks out with the new-comer: always providing she is sufficiently attractive, and that she will consent to walk. It is remarkable, however, that most of the girls are quite comely, they are all young, and this roving life aboard the car gives them a sailor's dash and recklessness. What matter how they behave when the ship is in port? Tomorrow they will be aboard again.

Annie, however, was something of a Tartar, and her sharp tongue had kept John Thomas at arm's length for many months. Perhaps, therefore, she liked him all the more: for he always came up smiling, with impudence. She watched him vanquish one girl, then another. She could tell by the movement of his mouth and eyes, when he flirted with her in the morning, that he had been walking out with this lass, or the other, the night before. A fine cock-of-the-walk he was. She could sum him up pretty well.

In this subtle antagonism they knew each other like old friends, they were as shrewd with one another almost as man and wife. But Annie had always kept him sufficiently at arm's length. Besides, she had a boy of her own.

The Statutes fair, however, came in November, at Bestwood. It happened that Annie had the Monday night off. It was a drizzling ugly night, yet she dressed herself up and went to the fair ground. She was alone, but she expected soon to find a pal of some sort.

The roundabouts were veering round and grinding out their music, the side-shows were making as much commotion as possible. In the coco-nut shies there were no coco-nuts, but artificial war-time substitutes, which the lads declared were fastened into the irons. There was a sad decline in brilliance and luxury. None the less, the ground was muddy as ever, there was the same crush, the press of faces lighted up by the flares and the electric lights, the same smell of naphtha and a few fried potatoes, and of electricity.

Who should be the first to greet Miss Annie on the show-ground but John Thomas. He had a black overcoat buttoned up to his chin, and a tweed cap pulled down over his brows, his face between was ruddy and smiling and handy as ever. She knew so well the way his mouth moved.

She was very glad to have a "boy". To be at the Statutes without a fellow was no fun. Instantly, like the gallant he was, he took her on the Dragons, grim-toothed, roundabout switchbacks. It was not nearly so exciting as a tram-car actually. But, then, to be seated in a shaking, green dragon, uplifted above the sea of bubble faces, careering in a rickety fashion in the lower heavens, whilst John Thomas leaned over her, his cigarette in his mouth, was after all the right style. She was a plump, quick, alive little creature. So she was quite excited and happy.

John Thomas made her stay on for the next round. And therefore she could hardly for shame repulse him when he put his arm around her and drew her a little nearer to him, in a very warm and cuddly manner. Besides, he was fairly discreet, he kept his movement as hidden as possible. She looked down, and saw that his red, clean hand was out of sight of the crowd. And they knew each other so well. So they warmed up to the fair.

After the dragons they went on the horses. John Thomas paid each time, so she could but be complaisant. He, of course, sat astride on the outer horse — named "Black Bess" — and she sat sideways, towards him, on the inner horse — named "Wildfire". But of course John Thomas was not going to sit discreetly on "Black Bess", holding the brass bar. Round they spun and heaved, in the light. And round he swung on his wooden steed, flinging one leg across her mount, and perilously tipping up and down, across the space, half lying back, laughing at her. He was perfectly happy; she was afraid her hat was on one side, but she was excited.

He threw quoits on a table, and won for her two large, pale blue hatpins. And then, hearing the noise of the cinemas, announcing another performance, they climbed the boards and went in.

Of course, during these performances pitch darkness falls from time to time, when the machine goes wrong. Then there is a wild whooping, and a loud smacking of simulated kisses. In these moments John Thomas drew Annie towards him. After all, he had a wonderfully warm, cosy way of holding a girl with his arm, he seemed to make such a nice fit. And, after all, it was pleasant to be so held; so very comforting and cosy and nice. He leaned over her and she felt his breath on her hair; she knew he wanted to kiss her on the lips. And, after all, he was so warm and she fitted in to him so softly. After all, she wanted him to touch her lips.

But the light sprang up; she also started electrically, and put her hat straight. He left his arm nonchalantly behind her. Well, it was fun, it was exciting to be at the Statutes with John Thomas.

When the cinema was over they went for a walk across the dark, damp fields. He had all the arts of love-making. He was especially good at holding a girl, when he sat with her on a stile in the black, drizzling darkness. He seemed to be holding her in space, against his own warmth and gratification. And his kisses were soft and slow and searching.

So Annie walked out with John Thomas, though she kept her own boy dangling in the distance. Some of the tram-girls chose to be huffy. But there, you must take things as you find them, in this life.

There was no mistake about it, Annie liked John Thomas a good deal. She felt so rich and warm in herself whenever he was near. And John Thomas really liked Annie, more than usual. The soft, melting way in which she could flow into a fellow, as if she melted into his very bones, was something rare and good. He fully appreciated this.

But with a developing acquaintance there began a developing intimacy. Annie wanted to consider him a person, a man: she wanted to take an intelligent interest in him, and to have an intelligent response. She did not want a mere nocturnal presence, which was what he was so far. And she prided herself that he could not leave her.

Here she made a mistake. John Thomas intended to remain a nocturnal presence; he had no idea of becoming an all-round individual to her. When she started to take an intelligent interest in him and his life and his character, he sheered off. He hated intelligent interest. And he knew that the only way to stop it was to avoid it. The possessive female was aroused in Annie. So he left her.

It is no use saying she was not surprised. She was at first startled, thrown out of her count. For she had been so *very* sure of holding him. For a while she was staggered, and everything became uncertain to her. Then she wept with fury, indignation, desolation, and misery. Then she had a spasm of despair. And then, when he came, still impudently, on to her car, still familiar, but letting her see by the movement of his head that he had gone away to somebody else for the time being, and was enjoying pastures new, then she determined to have her own back.

She had a very shrewd idea what girls John Thomas had taken out. She went to Nora Purdy. Nora was a tall, rather pale, but well-built girl, with beautiful yellow hair. She was rather secretive.

"Hey!" said Annie, accosting her; then softly: "Who's John Thomas on with now?"

"I don't know," said Nora.

"Why, tha does," said Annie, ironically lapsing into dialect. "Tha knows as well as I do."

"Well, I do, then," said Nora. "It isn't me, so don't bother."

"It's Cissy Meakin, isn't it?"

"It is, for all I know."

"Hasn't he got a face on him!" said Annie. "I don't half like his cheek. I could knock him off the footboard when he comes round at me."

"He'll get dropped on one of these days," said Nora.

"Ay, he will, when somebody makes up their mind to drop it on him. I should like to see him taken down a peg or two, shouldn't you?"

"I shouldn't mind," said Nora.

"You've got quite as much cause to as I have," said Annie. "But we'll drop on him one of these days, my girl. What? Don't you want to?"

"I don't mind," said Nora.

But as a matter of fact, Nora was much more vindictive than Annie.

One by one Annie went the round of the old flames. It so happened that Cissy Meakin left the tramway service in quite a short time. Her mother made her leave. Then John Thomas was on the *qui vive*. He cast his eyes over his old flock. And his eyes lighted on Annie. He thought she would be safe now. Besides, he liked her.

She arranged to walk home with him on Sunday night. It so happened that her car would be in the depot at half-past nine: the last car would come in at 10.15. So John Thomas was to wait for her there.

At the depot the girls had a little waiting-room of their own. It was quite rough, but cosy, with a fire and an oven and a mirror, and table and wooden chairs. The half-dozen girls who knew John Thomas only too well had arranged to take service this Sunday afternoon. So, as the cars began to come in, early, the girls dropped into the waiting-room. And instead of hurrying off home, they sat around the fire and had a cup of tea. Outside was the darkness and lawlessness of war-time.

John Thomas came on the car after Annie, at about a quarter to ten. He poked his head easily into the girls' waiting-room.

"Prayer-meeting?" he asked.

"Ay," said Laura Sharp. "Ladies only."

"That's me!" said John Thomas. It was one of his favourite exclamations.

"Shut the door, boy," said Muriel Baggaley.

"On which side of me?" said John Thomas.

"Which tha likes," said Polly Birkin.

He had come in and closed the door behind him. The girls moved in their circle, to make a place for him near the fire. He took off his great-coat and pushed back his hat.

"Who handles the teapot?" he said.

Nora Purdy silently poured him out a cup of tea.

"Want a bit o' my bread and drippin'?" said Muriel Baggaley to him.

"Ay, give us a bit."

And he began to eat his piece of bread.

"There's no place like home, girls," he said.

They all looked at him as he uttered this piece of impudence. He seemed to be sunning himself in the presence of so many damsels.

"Especially if you're not afraid to go home in the dark," said Laura Sharp.

"Me! By myself I am."

They sat till they heard the last tram come in. In a few minutes Emma Houselay entered.

"Come on, my old duck!" cried Polly Birkin.

"It *is* perishing," said Emma, holding her fingers to the fire.

"But — I'm afraid to, go home in, the dark," sang Laura Sharp, the tune having got into her mind.

"Who're you going home with tonight, John Thomas?" asked Muriel Baggaley, coolly.

"Tonight?" said John Thomas. "Oh, I'm going home by myself tonight — all on my lonely-o."

"That's me!" said Nora Purdy, using his own ejaculation.

The girls laughed shrilly.

"Me as well, Nora," said John Thomas.

"Don't know what you mean," said Laura.

"Yes, I'm toddling," said he, rising and reaching for his overcoat.

"Nay," said Polly, "We're all here waiting for you."

"We've got to be up in good time in the morning," he said, in the benevolent official manner.

They all laughed.

"Nay," said Muriel. "Don't leave us all lonely, John Thomas. Take one!"

"I'll take the lot, if you like," he responded gallantly.

"That you won't, either," said Muriel. "Two's company; seven's too much of a good thing."

"Nay — take one," said Laura. "Fair and square, all above board and say which."

"Ay," cried Annie, speaking for the first time. "Pick, John Thomas; let's hear thee."

"Nay," he said. "I'm going home quiet tonight. Feeling good, for once."

"Whereabouts?" said Annie. "Take a good 'un, then. But tha's got to take one of us!"

"Nay, how can I take one," he said, laughing uneasily. "I don't want to make enemies."

"You'd only make *one*," said Annie.

"The chosen *one*," added Laura.

"Oh, my! Who said girls!" exclaimed John Thomas, again turning, as if to escape. "Well — good night."

"Nay, you've got to make your pick," said Muriel. "Turn your face to the wall, and say which one touches you. Go on — we shall only just touch your back — one of us. Go on — turn your face to the wall, and don't look, and say which one touches you."

He was uneasy, mistrusting them. Yet he had not the courage to break away. They pushed him to a wall and stood him there with his face to it. Behind his back they all grimaced, tittering. He looked so comical. He looked around uneasily.

"Go on!" he cried.

"You're looking — you're looking!" they shouted.

He turned his head away. And suddenly, with a movement like a swift cat, Annie went forward and fetched him a box on the side of the head that sent his cap flying and himself staggering. He started round.

But at Annie's signal they all flew at him, slapping him, pinching him, pulling his hair, though more in fun than in spite or anger. He, however, saw red. His blue eyes flamed with strange fear as well as fury, and he butted through the girls to the door. It was locked. He wrenched at it. Roused, alert, the girls stood around and looked at him, He faced them, at bay. At that moment they were rather horrifying to him, as they stood in their short uniforms. He was distinctly afraid.

"Come on, John Thomas! Come on! Choose!" said Annie.

"What are you after? Open the door," he said.

"We shan't — not till you've chosen!" said Muriel.

"Chosen what?" he said.

"Chosen the one you're going to marry," she replied.

He hesitated a moment.

"Open the blasted door," he said, "and get back to your senses." He spoke with official authority.

"You've got to choose!" cried the girls.

"Come on!" cried Annie, looking him in the eye. "Come on! Come on!"

He went forward, rather vaguely. She had taken off her belt, and swinging it, she fetched him a sharp blow over the head with the buckle end. He sprang and seized her. But immediately the other girls rushed upon him, pulling and tearing and beating him. Their blood was now thoroughly up. He was their sport now. They were going to have their own back, out of him. Strange, wild creatures, they hung on him and rushed at him to bear him down. His tunic was torn right up his back, Nora had hold at the back of his collar, and was actually strangling him. Luckily the button burst. He struggled in a wild frenzy of fury and terror, almost mad terror. His tunic was simply torn off his back, his shirt-sleeves were torn away, his arms were naked. The girls rushed at him, clenched their hands on him and pulled at him: or they rushed at him and pushed him, butted him with all their might: or they struck him wild blows. He ducked and cringed and struck sideways. They became more intense.

At last he was down. They rushed on him, kneeling on him. He had neither breath nor strength to move. His face was bleeding with a long scratch, his brow was bruised.

Annie knelt on him, the other girls knelt and hung on to him. Their faces were flushed, their hair wild, their eyes were all glittering strangely. He lay at last quite still, with face averted, as an animal lies when it is defeated and at the mercy of the captor. Sometimes his eye glanced back at the wild faces of the girls. His breath rose heavily, his wrists were torn. "Now then, my fellow!" gasped Annie at length. "Now then — now — " At the sound of her terrifying, cold triumph, he suddenly started to struggle as an animal might, but the girls threw themselves upon him with unnatural strength and power, forcing him down.

"Yes — now, then!" gasped Annie at length.

And there was a dead silence, in which the thud of heart-beating was to be heard. It was a suspense of pure silence in every soul.

"Now you know where you are," said Annie.

The sight of his white, bare arm maddened the girls. He lay in a kind of trance of fear and antagonism. They felt themselves filled with supernatural strength.

Suddenly Polly started to laugh — to giggle wildly — helplessly — and Emma and Muriel joined in. But Annie and Nora and Laura remained the same, tense, watchful, with gleaming eyes. He winced away from these eyes.

"Yes," said Annie, in a curious low tone, secret and deadly. "Yes! You've got it now. You know what you've done, don't you? You know what you've done."

He made no sound nor sign, but lay with bright, averted eyes, and averted, bleeding face.

"You ought to be *killed*, that's what you ought," said Annie, tensely. "You ought to be *killed*." And there was a terrifying lust in her voice.

Polly was ceasing to laugh, and giving long-drawn Oh-h-hs and sighs as she came to herself.

"He's got to choose," she said vaguely.

"Oh, yes, he has," said Laura, with vindictive decision.

"Do you hear — do you hear?" said Annie. And with a sharp movement, that made him wince, she turned his face to her.

"Do you hear?" she repeated, shaking him.

But he was quite dumb. She fetched him a sharp slap on the face. He started, and his eyes widened. Then his face darkened with defiance after all.

"Do you hear?" she repeated.

He only looked at her with hostile eyes.

"Speak!" she said, putting her face devilishly near his.

"What?" he said, almost overcome.

"You've got to *choose*!" she cried, as if it were some terrible menace, and as if it hurt her that she could not exact more.

"What?" he said, in fear.

"Choose your girl, Coddy. You've got to choose her now. And you'll get your neck broken if you play any more of your tricks, my boy. You're settled now."

There was a pause. Again he averted his face. He was cunning in his overthrow. He did not give in to them really — no, not if they tore him to bits.

"All right, then," he said, "I choose Annie." His voice was strange and full of malice. Annie let go of him as if he had been a hot coal.

"He's chosen Annie!" said the girls in chorus.

"Me!" cried Annie. She was still kneeling, but away from him. He was still lying prostrate, with averted face. The girls grouped uneasily ground.

"Me!" repeated Annie, with a terrible bitter accent.

Then she got up, drawing away from him with strange disgust and bitterness.

"I wouldn't touch him," she said.

But her face quivered with a kind of agony, she seemed as if she would fall. The other girls turned aside. He remained lying on the floor, with his torn clothes and bleeding, averted face.

"Oh, if he's chosen — " said Polly.

"I don't want him — he can choose again," said Annie, with the same rather bitter hopelessness.

"Get up," said Polly, lifting his shoulder. "Get up."

He rose slowly, a strange, ragged, dazed creature. The girls eyed him from a distance, curiously, furtively, dangerously.

"Who wants him?" cried Laura, roughly.

"Nobody," they answered, with contempt. Yet each one of them waited for him to look at her, hoped he would look at her. All except Annie, and something was broken in her.

He, however, kept his face closed and averted from them all. There was a silence of the end. He picked up the torn pieces of his tunic, without knowing what to do with them. The girls stood about uneasily, flushed, panting, tidying their hair and their dress unconsciously, and watching him. He looked at none of them. He espied his cap in a corner, and went and picked it up. He put it on his head, and one of the girls burst into a shrill, hysteric laugh at the sight he presented. He, however, took no heed, but went straight to where his overcoat hung on a peg. The girls moved away from contact with him as if he had been an electric wire. He put on his coat and buttoned it down. Then he rolled his tunic-rags into a bundle, and stood before the locked door, dumbly.

"Open the door, somebody," said Laura.

"Annie's got the key," said one.

Annie silently offered the key to the girls. Nora unlocked the door.

"Tit for tat, old man," she said. "Show yourself a man, and don't bear a grudge."

But without a word or sign he had opened the door and gone, his face closed, his head dropped.

"That'll learn him," said Laura.

"Coddy!" said Nora.

"Shut up, for God's sake!" cried Annie fiercely, as if in torture.

"Well, I'm about ready to go, Polly. Look sharp!" said Muriel.

The girls were all anxious to be off. They were tidying themselves hurriedly, with mute, stupefied faces.

COMMENTARY

The first thing that strikes one about a story by D. H. Lawrence is that it is literally his. From the first word to the last it is Lawrentian, by a totality of creation which, artificially but conveniently for criticism, we may break down into content and expression. It must always be remembered that this is the critic's not the creator's analysis: *Tickets, Please* is, wholly and indivisibly, of Lawrence. Others may write about the Midlands, they may write a story of this particular tram-way and of those who worked there during the First World War. They will not, they cannot, write it as Lawrence does. The reason is that Lawrence, of all writers, writes as he must — both in matter and manner.

This absolute fidelity to his own vision — to his daimon, as he puts it — is the first determinant of anything written by Lawrence. He refuses to accommodate either his matter or his style to any accepted or conventional notions. For him it is nonsense to say "A short story must have … " A story by him is always what it has to be by that inner compulsion, by that integrity of vision and expression. (Consider *Tickets, Please* with these two ideas in mind. Remember that Lawrence was a miner's son, that he grew up at Eastwood, not far from Nottingham, at the close of the nineteenth and the beginning of the twentieth century, and that he knew the working and lower middle class as few writers of eminence have done. What evidence of this distinctive social awareness is there in this story?)

Nothing could be further from Lawrence's conception of the short story than the idea of a nicely contrived or complicated plot. A story by him has organic form. It begins, it grows from within and it ends absolutely naturally. Yet there is a controlling purpose in this unforced sequence. (Notice in *Tickets, Please* the gradual narrowing of focus:

general picture of this wartime tramway system; Annie and John Thomas seen as typical of relationships within this little world; the transition from fellowship to hostility; the culmination of this hostility in the frenzied attack on John Thomas.)

Lawrence drew directly for his material from the world he knew, but his story is not just reportage. He is not writing as a skilled journalist doing a series of stories called "Inside Bestwood" or "The Real Midlands". ("Actuality, not social comment" — how would you show the truth of this remark about *Tickets, Please?*) What, then, is the "point" of this story?

The answer to this question will take you straight into what is central in the whole of Lawrence's writing. It is the relations of men and women. Infinitely varied as these are, they are yet reducible to two terms — attraction and antagonism. (How is this duality shown in the relations of Annie and John Thomas and of John Thomas and the other girl conductors?)

Tickets, Please shows another and closely connected aspect of this basic feature of Lawrence's way of presenting life. He is, to a degree unmatched by any other writer, sensitive to the distinctive mode of feeling of men and women. (Observe the little turns of behaviour or of talk that show this, e.g. John Thomas and Annie at the Statutes fair. Why has Lawrence put in this section? What does it grow out of and what does it lead to?) Equally distinctive of Lawrence is his awareness of the possessiveness of love. Can you see where this is constructively used in *Tickets, Please?*

It is sometimes said of Lawrence that he does not, even that he cannot, "create characters". What do you think is meant by this remark? Is it not the fact, as is shown in this story, that he can create *persons?* We feel them as individuals written about, not as concepts projected from a story-teller's imagination. What are the means by which Lawrence does this, at least for Annie and John Thomas?

As with his matter — what he chooses from experience — so with his manner of writing. It is marked by freshness and directness. Examine closely the first paragraph of this story. Why that long first sentence? In what sense is it exactly right for introducing this Midlands tram-way system? Have you noticed the deliberate repetition of a descriptive phrase? Where does Lawrence use an unexpected but effective image? How does the movement of the prose serve to reinforce the matter of the paragraph? The passages of conversation also merit attention, especially the exchanges between John Thomas and the revengeful girls. (Notice how unforced it is; how it matches the primitive quality of the passions unleashed; how economical and dramatic it is.)

D. H. Lawrence has always divided sharply his readers. On the evidence of *Tickets, Please* what do you think has been charged against him and what qualities would you adduce in his defence?

6

GEORGE ORWELL

1903-1950

GEORGE ORWELL was the pseudonym of Eric Hugh Blair, born in Bengal 1903. The choice of this pen-name (1930) is not without interest, for it is the coupling of a country name with that of a Suffolk river; and George Orwell, who for a while in his chequered career ran a small general store in the country, will always be associated, as man and writer, with that which he cherished in the English tradition — justice, freedom, respect for the individual.

Of his schooling at Eton, which he entered with a scholarship, Orwell said that it had not been "much of a formative influence". Then came five years with the Imperial Police in Burma. "I gave it up partly because the climate had ruined my health, partly because I already had vague ideas of writing books, but mainly because I could not go on any longer serving an imperialism which I had come to regard very largely as a racket." (You may look for corroborative evidence in *Shooting An Elephant*.) He then spent about a year and a half in Paris, "writing novels and stories which no one would publish". There followed several years of fairly severe poverty, in the course of which Orwell worked as a dishwasher, a private tutor, and a teacher in cheap private schools. In 1936 he served with the forces of the Left against Franco in the Spanish Civil War and was rather badly wounded. By this time he was recognized as a writer of ability and until his death in 1950 he withdrew from public affairs in order the better to write of them. His political satires *Animal Farm* (1945) and *Nineteen Eighty-Four* established his world-wide fame.

Orwell was a writer wholly "committed" or "engaged", as we term one who believes that he must, as a creative artist, be concerned with the fundamental issues of his day. "Every line of serious work that

I have written since 1936 has been written, directly or indirectly, against totalitarianism and for democratic socialism, as I understand it." Moreover, for Orwell, there was a very real connection between literary values and political morality — "To write in plain, vigorous language one has to think fearlessly, and if one thinks fearlessly one cannot be politically orthodox." One of Orwell's most characteristic essays is on "Politics and the English Language", in which he gives counsel we should all heed:

1. Never use a metaphor, simile or other figure of speech which you are used to seeing in print.
2. Never use a long word where a short one will do.
3. If it is possible to cut a word out, always cut it out.
4. Never use the passive where you can use the active.
5. Never use a foreign phrase, a scientific word or a jargon word if you can think of an everyday English equivalent.
6. Break any of these rules sooner than say anything outright barbarous.

Suggested Reading: *Down and Out in Paris and London* (1933); *The Road to Wigan Pier* (1937); *Animal Farm* (1945); *Nineteen Eighty-Four* (1949); *Shooting An Elephant* (1950); *Such, Such were the Joys* (1953).

*   *   *

Shooting an Elephant

IN Moulmein, in Lower Burma, I was hated by large numbers of people — the only time in my life that I have been important enough for this to happen to me. I was subdivisional police officer of the town, and in an aimless, petty kind of way anti-European feeling was very bitter. No one had the guts to raise a riot, but if a European woman went through the bazaars alone somebody would probably spit betel juice over her dress. As a police officer I was an obvious target and was baited whenever it seemed safe to do so. When a nimble Burman tripped me up on the football field and the referee (another Burman) looked the other way, the crowd yelled with hideous laughter. This happened more than once. In the end the sneering yellow faces of young men that met me everywhere, the insults hooted after me when I was at a safe distance, got badly on my nerves. The young Buddhist priests were the worst of all. There were several thousands of them in the town and none of them seemed to have anything to do except stand on street corners and jeer at Europeans.

All this was perplexing and upsetting. For at that time I had already made up my mind that imperialism was an evil thing and the sooner I chucked up my job and got out of it the better. Theoretically — and secretly, of course — I was all for the Burmese and all against their oppressors, the British. As for the job I was doing, I hated it more bitterly than I can perhaps make clear. In a job like that you can see the dirty work of Empire at close quarters. The wretched prisoners huddling in the stinking cages of the lock-ups, the grey, cowed faces of the long-term convicts, the scarred buttocks of the men who had been flogged with bamboos — all these oppressed me with an intolerable sense of guilt. But I could get nothing into perspective. I was young and ill-educated and I had had to think out my problems in the utter silence that is imposed on every Englishman in the East. I did not even know that the British Empire is dying, still less did I know that it is a great deal better than the younger empires that are going to supplant it. All I knew was that I was stuck between my hatred of the empire I served and my rage against the evil-spirited little beasts who tried to make my job impossible. With one part of my mind I thought of the British Raj as an unbreakable tyranny, as something clamped down, *in saecula saeculorum*, upon the will of prostrate peoples; with another part I thought that the greatest joy in the world would be to drive a bayonet into a Buddhist priest's guts. Feelings like these are the normal by-products of imperialism; ask any Indian official, if you can catch him off duty.

One day something happened which in a roundabout way was enlightening. It was a tiny incident in itself, but it gave me a better glimpse than I had had before of the real nature of imperialism — the real motives for which despotic governments act. Early one morning the sub-inspector at a police station the other end of the town rang me up on the 'phone and said that an elephant was ravaging the bazaar. Would I please come and do something about it? I did not know what

I could do, but I wanted to see what was happening and I got on to a pony and started out. I took my rifle, an old .44 Winchester and much too small to kill an elephant, but I thought the noise might be useful *in terrorem*. Various Burmans stopped me on the way and told me about the elephant's doings. It was not, of course, a wild elephant, but a tame one which had gone "must". It had been chained up as tame elephants always are when their attack of "must" is due, but on the previous night it had broken its chain and escaped. Its mahout, the only person who could manage it when it was in that state, had set out in pursuit, but he had taken the wrong direction and was now twelve hours' journey away, and in the morning the elephant had suddenly reappeared in the town. The Burmese population had no weapons and were quite helpless against it. It had already destroyed somebody's bamboo hut, killed a cow and raided fruit-stalls and devoured the stock; also it had met the municipal rubbish van, and, when the driver jumped out and took to his heels, had turned the van over and inflicted violences upon it.

The Burmese sub-inspector and some Indian constables were waiting for me in the quarter where the elephant had been seen. It was a very poor quarter, a labyrinth of squalid bamboo huts, thatched with palm-leaf, winding all over a steep hillside. I remember that it was a cloudy stuffy morning at the beginning of the rains. We began questioning the people as to where the elephant had gone, and, as usual, failed to get any definite information. That is invariably the case in the East; a story always sounds clear enough at a distance, but the nearer you get to the scene of events the vaguer it becomes. Some of the people said that the elephant had gone in one direction, some said that he had gone in another, some professed not even to have heard of any elephant. I had almost made up my mind that the whole story was a pack of lies, when we heard yells a little distance away. There was a loud scandalized cry of "Go away, child! Go away this instant!" and an old woman with a switch in her hand came round the corner of a hut, violently shooing away a crowd of naked children. Some more women followed, clicking their tongues and exclaiming; evidently there was something there that the children ought not to have seen. I rounded the hut and saw a man's dead body sprawling in the mud. He was an Indian, a black Dravidian coolie, almost naked, and he could not have been dead many minutes. The people said that the elephant had come suddenly upon him round the corner of the hut, caught him with its trunk, put its foot on his back and ground him into the earth. This was the rainy season and the ground was soft, and his face had scored a trench a foot deep and a couple of yards long. He was lying on his belly with arms crucified and head sharply twisted to one side. His face was coated with mud, the eyes wide open, the teeth bared and grinning with an expression of unendurable agony. (Never tell me, by the way, that the dead look peaceful. Most of the corpses I have seen looked devilish.) The friction of the great beast's foot had stripped the skin from his back as neatly as one skins a rabbit. As soon as I saw the dead man I sent an orderly to a friend's house near by to borrow an elephant rifle. I had already sent back the pony, not wanting it to go mad with fright and throw me if it smelled the elephant.

The orderly came back in a few minutes with a rifle and five cartridges, and meanwhile some Burmans had arrived and told us that the elephant was in the paddy fields below, only a few hundred yards away. As I started forward practically the whole population of the quarter flocked out of the houses and followed me. They had seen the rifle and were all shouting excitedly that I was going to shoot the elephant. They had not shown much interest in the elephant when he was merely ravaging their homes, but it was different now that he was going to be shot. It was a bit of fun to them, as it would be to an English crowd; besides, they wanted the meat. It made me vaguely uneasy. I had no intention of shooting the elephant — I had merely sent for the rifle to defend myself if necessary — and it is always unnerving to have a crowd following you. I marched down the hill, looking and feeling a fool, with the rifle over my shoulder and an ever-growing army of people jostling at my heels. At the bottom, when you got away from the huts, there was a metalled road and beyond that a miry waste of paddy fields a thousand yards across, not yet ploughed but soggy from the first rains and dotted with coarse grass. The elephant was standing eighty yards from the road, his left side towards us. He took not the slightest notice of the crowd's approach. He was tearing up bunches of grass, beating them against his knees to clean them and stuffing them into his mouth.

I had halted on the road. As soon as I saw the elephant I knew with perfect certainty that I ought not to shoot him. It is a serious matter to shoot a working elephant — it is comparable to destroying a huge and costly piece of machinery — and obviously one ought not to do it if it can possibly be avoided. And at that distance, peacefully eating, the elephant looked no more dangerous than a cow. I thought then and I think now that his attack of "must" was already passing off; in which case he would merely wander harmlessly about until the mahout came back and caught him. Moreover, I did not in the least want to shoot him. I decided that I would watch him for a little while to make sure that he did not turn savage again, and then go home.

But at that moment I glanced round at the crowd that had followed me. It was an immense crowd, two thousand at the least and growing every minute. It blocked the road for a long distance on either side. I looked at the sea of yellow faces above the garish clothes — faces all happy and excited over this bit of fun, all certain that the elephant was going to be shot. They were watching me as they would watch a conjuror about to perform a trick. They did not like me, but with the magical rifle in my hands I was momentarily worth watching. And suddenly I realized that I should have to shoot the elephant after all. The people expected it of me and I had got to do it; I could feel their two thousand wills pressing me forward, irresistibly. And it was at this moment, as I stood there with the rifle in my hands, that I first grasped the hollowness, the futility of the white man's dominion in the East. Here was I, the white man with his gun, standing in front of the unarmed native crowd — seemingly the leading actor of the piece; but in reality I was only an absurd puppet pushed to and fro by the will of those yellow faces behind. I perceived in this moment that when the white man turns tyrant it is his own freedom that he destroys. He becomes a sort of hollow, posing dummy, the conventionalized figure of a sahib. For it is the condition of his rule that he shall spend his life in trying to impress the "natives", and so in every crisis he has got to do what the "natives" expect of him. He wears a mask, and his face grows to fit it. I had got to shoot the elephant. I had committed myself to doing it when I sent for the rifle. A sahib has got to act like a sahib; he has got to appear resolute, to know his own mind and do definite things. To come all that way, rifle in hand, with two thousand people marching at my heels, and then to trail feebly away, having done nothing — no, that was impossible. The crowd would laugh at me. And my whole life, every white man's life in the East, was one long struggle not to be laughed at.

But I did not want to shoot the elephant. I watched him beating his bunch of grass against his knees, with that preoccupied grandmotherly air that elephants have. It seemed to me that it would be murder to shoot him. At that age I was not squeamish about killing animals, but I had never shot an elephant and never wanted to. (Somehow it always seems worse to kill a *large* animal.) Besides, there was the beast's owner to be considered. Alive, the elephant was worth at least a hundred pounds; dead, he would only be worth the value of his tusks — five pounds, possibly. But I had got to act quickly. I turned to some experienced-looking Burmans who had been there when we arrived, and asked them how the elephant had been behaving. They all said the same thing: he took no notice of you if you left him alone, but he might charge you if you went too close to him.

It was perfectly clear to me what I ought to do. I ought to walk up to within, say, twenty-five yards of the elephant and test his behaviour. If he charged I could shoot, if he took no notice of me it would be safe to leave him until the mahout came back. But also I knew that I was going to do no such thing. I was a poor shot with a rifle and the ground was soft mud into which one would sink at every step. If the elephant charged and I missed him, I should have as much chance as a toad under a steam-roller. But even then I was not thinking particularly of my own skin, only of the watchful yellow faces behind. For at that moment, with the crowd watching me, I was not afraid in the ordinary sense, as I would have been if I had been alone. A white man mustn't be frightened in front of "natives"; and so, in general, he isn't frightened. The sole thought in my mind was that if anything went wrong those two thousand Burmans would see me pursued, caught, trampled on and reduced to a grinning corpse like that Indian up the hill. And if that happened it was quite probable that some of them would laugh. That would never do. There was only one alternative. I shoved the cartridges into the magazine and lay down on the road to get a better aim.

The crowd grew very still, and a deep, low, happy sigh, as of people who see the theatre curtain go up at last, breathed from innumerable throats. They were going to have their bit of fun after all. The rifle was a beautiful German thing with cross-hair sights. I did not then know that in shooting an elephant one should shoot to cut an imaginary bar running from ear-hole to ear-hole. I ought, therefore, as the elephant was sideways on, to have aimed straight at his ear-hole; actually I aimed several inches in front of this, thinking the brain would be further forward.

When I pulled the trigger I did not hear the bang or feel the kick — one never does when a shot goes home — but I heard the devilish roar of glee that went up from the crowd. In that instant, in too short a time, one would have thought, even for the bullet to get there, a mysterious, terrible change had come over the elephant. He neither stirred nor fell, but every line of his body had altered. He looked suddenly stricken, shrunken, immensely old, as though the frightful impact of the bullet had paralysed him without knocking him down. At last, after what seemed a long time — it might have been five seconds, I dare say — he sagged flabbily to his knees. His mouth slobbered. An enormous senility seemed to have settled upon him. One could have imagined him thousands of years old. I fired again into the same spot. At the second shot he did not collapse but climbed with desperate slowness to his feet and stood weakly upright, with legs sagging and head dropping. I fired a third time. That was the shot that did for him. You could see the agony of it jolt his whole body and knock the last remnant of strength from his legs. But in falling he seemed for a moment to rise, for as his hind legs collapsed beneath him he seemed to tower upwards like a huge rock toppling, his trunk reaching skyward like a tree. He trumpeted, for the first and only time. And then down he came, his belly towards me, with a crash that seemed to shake the ground even where I lay.

I got up. The Burmans were already racing past me across the mud. It was obvious that the elephant would never rise again, but he was not dead. He was breathing very rhythmically with long rattling gasps, his great mound of a side painfully rising and falling. His mouth was wide open — I could see far down into caverns of pale pink throat. I waited a long time for him to die, but his breathing did not weaken. Finally I fired my two remaining shots into the spot where I thought his heart must be. The thick blood welled out of him like red velvet, but still

96

he did not die. His body did not even jerk when the shots hit him, the tortured breathing continued without a pause. He was dying, very slowly and in great agony, but in some world remote from me where not even a bullet could damage him further. I felt that I had got to put an end to that dreadful noise. It seemed dreadful to see the great beast lying there, powerless to move and yet powerless to die, and not even to be able to finish him. I sent back for my small rifle and poured shot after shot into his heart and down his throat. They seemed to make no impression. The tortured gasps continued as steadily as the ticking of a clock.

In the end I could not stand it any longer and went away. I heard later that it took him half an hour to die. Burmans were arriving with dahs and baskets even before I left, and I was told they had stripped his body almost to the bones by the afternoon.

Afterwards, of course, there were endless discussions about the shooting of the elephant. The owner was furious, but he was only an Indian and could do nothing. Besides, legally I had done the right thing, for a mad elephant has to be killed, like a mad dog, if its owner fails to control it. Among the Europeans opinion was divided. The older men said I was right, the younger men said it was a damn shame to shoot an elephant for killing a coolie, because an elephant was worth more than any damn Coringhee coolie. And afterwards I was very glad that the coolie had been killed: it put me legally in the right and it gave me a sufficient pretext for shooting the elephant. I often wondered whether any of the others grasped that I had done it solely to avoid looking a fool.

COMMENTARY

It can be assumed that George Orwell, when writing this record of his experience in Burma, had not the conscious intention of writing a short story. His first object — we may be certain of this from a reading of his various autobiographical and critical writings — was to set down the truth. Orwell's nature, as man and as writer, was to be absolutely honest — with himself and with his readers. Nothing would be further from his mind than the "thinking up" of an incident which would be the nucleus of a short story. Equally remote would be the thought that he ought to conform to some pattern that was regarded as right or necessary for the short story. In *Shooting an Elephant* we have, in fact, a piece of reporting that happens — but happens only because of Orwell's sure handling — to be as truly a short story as any in this collection.

Now why is this? Can you see what it is that makes this factual record as rightly to be regarded as a short story as *Paste* — to take an example from the opposite end of the spectrum of the short story? One or two answers suggest themselves at once: the absolute unity of the whole; the technique whereby the reader is first interested in the narrator and his circumstances, and then held by the mounting excitement of the critical situation with which, relatively inexperienced, Orwell has to deal; the feeling we have that there is more in this account than the mere action of destroying the elephant, fascinating though that is.

Even a first uncritical reading will leave the reader with a sense that the anecdote — for in a way that is all it is — has somehow become the vehicle for so much more than an exciting record of an event that must, of its very nature, be outside the life of all but a few. What is this "something more"? You may say that it is the directness and completeness with which Orwell's personal feelings are conveyed. (What image of the man have you formed from this record? What different aspects of Orwell's thoughts and feelings are revealed? In what way does he show himself different from the conventional idea of a British official overseas?)

Next you may begin to realize that throughout the story there is being shown an attitude to life and, within this, a judgment made upon much, e.g. imperialism, that by many is uncritically accepted. (Can you think of stories where "the British Raj" and its officials are shown in a very different light?) You might note which you think the severest or the most penetrating of Orwell's critical animadversions upon the reality beneath the glamour of Empire.

It must be remembered, however, that these serious observations are never uttered in the shrill or strident tones of carping denigration. You should ask yourself how Orwell secures greater effect by subordinating these intensely felt reflections on imperialism to their appropriate place in the total interest of *Shooting an Elephant*.

Now consider the technique shown in the composition and balance of this unified piece of writing. What is the exact function of the first two paragraphs? What would the whole lose, if these were omitted? How and at what later points in the story are we reminded of them?

Once the elephant and the alarm have been introduced notice how time and again Orwell reminds us of the dilemma in which he found himself. Indeed his situation and his reactions to it afford an example of a fundamental problem which can be seen by asking "Was Orwell free to shoot or not to shoot the elephant?" From the evidence of the story what answer would you give to this question?

The integrity of a man is a moral issue. It is also a literary one. Orwell's manner of writing is a reflection of what he was. Look now at the prose of *Shooting an Elephant*. What are the characteristics of the style? Immediacy and simplicity. But how are these secured? (Study the choice of word and phrase; the form and length of the sentences; the use of the added or parenthetical thought which gives a sudden depth to its context; the rare but striking image.)

Some stories we re-read because of their intrinsic interest and we are hardly conscious of their author; *Shooting an Elephant* we re-read because, in addition to the unfailing grip of the narrative, we are drawn to the forthright and mature personality of George Orwell.

7

FRANK O'CONNOR
(pseudonym of Michael O'Donovan)
1903-

ANOTHER specialist in the short story form, and one of the acknowledged living masters of the art; though he has also published verse, plays, and criticism.

He was born in Cork, and attended the Christian Brothers' school there, but was too poor to go to university. A professional attitude to literature showed itself early: at twelve he had already put together a "collected edition" of his work — which did not, however, include short stories. We have his word for it that his early writings was done in Erse.

For some years he worked as a librarian, first in County Cork and then in Dublin, meanwhile continuing to write. While in Dublin he attracted the notice of the then mentor of Irish letters "Æ", who accepted his stories for the *Irish Statesman* and in 1931 proclaimed him the most important find among Irish writers since James Stephens. In that year appeared the first of his many collections of short stories, *Guests of the Nation*, which established him as an author. He was subsequently, for a time, a director of the celebrated Abbey Theatre in Dublin, and acquired from that experience, as he tells us, "a lasting passion for techniques". Technical finesse has remained a marked (but not obvious) characteristic of his work.

Yeats once said of O'Connor that he "is doing for Ireland what Chekhov did for Russia". O'Connor is far from singular among craftsmen of the short story in claiming Chekhov as a master, but he has perhaps closer affinities than most with the great Russian. They share a literary concern with events in patriarchal peasant societies (probably what Yeats had in mind). They show a like interest in and approach to technical problems; summed up by O'Connor in the illuminating observation that Chekhov had what he himself strove for, "the completely organic form". Above all, there is an evident similarity in their overall conception of the short story:

> Story telling is the nearest thing one can get to the quality of a pure lyric poem. It doesn't deal with problems; it doesn't have any solution to offer; it just states the human condition.

This holds as beautifully for Chekhov's art as it does for that of O'Connor himself; and its force is by no means confined to the short story.

O'Connor says of himself that he prefers to write in the mornings, and sometimes writes in the evenings, but likes to leave his afternoons free to cycle, walk, look in bookshops, and talk. He is interested in architecture and eighteenth-century music, though his main recreation is cycling, the extent of his devotion to which is displayed by his one recorded complaint against America — that it has no cycling tracks.

Suggested Reading: *Guests of the Nation* (1931); *Bones of Contention* (1936); *Selected Stories* (1946); *More Stories* (1954).

*   *   *

In the Train

"THERE!" said the sergeant's wife. "You would hurry me."

"I always like to be in time for a train," replied the sergeant with the equability of one who has many times before explained the guiding principle of his existence.

"I'd have had heaps of time to buy the hat," added his wife.

The sergeant sighed and opened his evening paper. His wife looked out on the dark platform, pitted with pale lights under which faces and faces passed, lit up and dimmed again. A uniformed lad strode up and down with a tray of periodicals and chocolates. Farther up the platform a drunken man was being seen off by his friends.

"I'm very fond of Michael O'Leary," he shouted. "He is the most sincere man I know."

"I have no life," sighed the sergeant's wife. "No life at all! There isn't a soul to speak to, nothing to look at all day but bogs and mountains and rain — always rain! And the people! Well, we've had a fine sample of them, haven't we?"

The sergeant continued to read.

"Just for the few days it's been like heaven. Such interesting people! Oh, I thought Mr Boyle had a glorious face! And his voice — it went through me."

The sergeant lowered his paper, took off his peaked cap, laid it on the seat beside him, and lit his pipe. He lit it in the old-fashioned way, ceremoniously, his eyes blinking pleasurably like a sleepy cat's in the match-flame. His wife scrutinized each face that passed, and it was plain that for her life meant faces and people and things and nothing more.

"Oh dear!" she said again. "I simply have no existence. I was educated in a convent and play the piano; my father was a literary man, and yet I am compelled to associate with the lowest types of humanity. If it was even a decent town, but a village!"

"Ah," said the sergeant, gapping his reply with anxious puffs, "maybe with God's help we'll get a shift one of these days." But he said it without conviction, and it was also plain that he was well pleased with himself, with the prospect of returning home, with his pipe and with his paper.

"Here are Magner and the others," said his wife as four other policemen passed the barrier. "I hope they'll have sense enough to let us alone ... How do you do? How do you do? Had a nice time, boys?" she called with sudden animation, and her pale, sullen face became warm and vivacious. The policemen smiled and touched their caps but did not halt.

"They might have stopped to say good evening," she added sharply, and her face sank into its old expression of boredom and dissatisfaction. "I don't think I'll ask Delancey to tea again. The others make an attempt, but really, Delancey is hopeless. When I smile and say 'Guard Delancey, wouldn't you like to use the butter-knife?' he just scowls at me from under his shaggy brows and says without a moment's hesitation, 'I would not.' "

"Ah, Delancey is a poor slob," said the sergeant affectionately.

"Oh, yes, but that's not enough, Jonathon. Slob or no slob, he should make an attempt. He's a young man; he should have a dinner-jacket at least. What sort of wife will he get if he won't even wear a dinner-jacket?"

"He's easy, I'd say. He's after a farm in Waterford!"

"Oh, a farm! A farm! The wife is only an incidental, I suppose?"

"Well, now from all I hear she's a damn' nice little incidental."

"Yes, I suppose many a nice little incidental came from a farm," answered his wife, raising her pale brows. But the irony was lost on him.

"Indeed, yes; indeed, yes," he said fervently.

"And here," she added in biting tones, "come our charming neighbours."

Into the pale lamplight stepped a group of peasants. Not such as one sees in the environs of a capital but in the mountains and along the coasts. Gnarled, wild, with turbulent faces, their ill-cut clothes full of character, the women in pale brown shawls, the men wearing black sombreros and carrying big sticks, they swept in, ill at ease, laughing and shouting defiantly. And, so much part of their natural environment were they, that for a moment they seemed to create about themselves rocks and bushes, tarns, turf-ricks and sea.

With a prim smile the sergeant's wife bowed to them through the open window.

"How do you do? How do you do?" she called. "Had a nice time?"

At the same moment the train gave a jolt and there was a rush in which the excited peasants were carried away. Some minutes passed; the influx of passengers almost ceased, and a porter began to slam the doors. The drunken man's voice rose in a cry of exultation.

"You can't possibly beat O'Leary!" he declared. "I'd lay down my life for Michael O'Leary."

Then, just as the train was about to start, a young woman in a brown shawl rushed through the barrier. The shawl, which came low enough to hide her eyes, she held firmly across her mouth, leaving visible only a long thin nose with a hint of pale flesh at either side. Beneath the shawl she was carrying a large parcel.

She looked hastily around, a porter shouted to her and pushed her towards the nearest compartment which happened to be that occupied by the sergeant and his wife. He had actually seized the handle of the door when the sergeant's wife sat up and screamed.

"Quick! Quick!" she cried. "Look who it is! She's coming in! Jonathon! Jonathon!"

The sergeant rose with a look of alarm on his broad red face. The porter threw open the door, with his free hand grasping the woman's elbow. But when she laid eyes on the sergeant's startled countenance, she stepped back, tore herself free, and ran crazily up the platform. The engine shrieked, the porter slammed the door with a curse, somewhere another door opened and shut, and the row of watchers, frozen into effigies of farewell, now dark now bright, began to glide gently past the window, and the stale, smoky air was charged with the breath of open fields.

2

The four policemen spread themselves out in a separate compartment and lit cigarettes.

"Ah, poor old Delancey!" said Magner with his reckless laugh. "He's cracked on her all right."

"Cracked on her," agreed Fox. "Did ye see the eye he gave her?"

Delancey smiled sheepishly. He was a tall, handsome, black-haired young man with the thick eyebrows described by the sergeant's wife. He was new to the force and suffered from a mixture of natural gentleness and country awkwardness.

"I am," he said in his husky voice, "cracked on her. The devil admire me, I never hated anyone yet, but I think I hate the living sight of her."

"Oh, now! Oh, now!" protested Magner.

"I do. I think the Almighty God must have put that one in the world with the one main object of persecuting me."

"Well, indeed," said Foley, "I don't know how the sergeant puts up with the same damsel. If any woman up and called me by an outlandish name like Jonathon when all knew my name was plain John, I'd do fourteen days for her — by God, I would, and a calendar month!"

The four men were now launched on a favourite topic that held them for more than an hour. None of them liked the sergeant's wife, and all had stories to tell against her. From these there emerged the fact that she was an incurable scandalmonger and mischief-maker, who couldn't keep quiet about her own business, much less that of her neighbours. And while they talked the train dragged across a dark plain, the heart of Ireland, and in the moonless night tiny cottage windows blew past like sparks from a fire, and a pale simulacrum of the lighted carriages leaped and frolicked over hedges and fields. Magner shut the window, and the compartment began to fill with smoke.

"She'll never rest till she's out of Farranchreesht," he said.

"That she mightn't!" groaned Delancey.

"How would you like the city yourself, Dan?" asked Magner.

"Man, dear," exclaimed Delancey with sudden brightness, "I'd like it fine. There's great life in a city."

"You can have it and welcome," said Foley, folding his hands across his paunch.

"Why so?"

"I'm well content where I am."

"But the life!"

"Ah, life be damned! What sort of life is it when you're always under someone's eye? Look at the poor devils in court!"

"True enough, true enough," said Fox.

"Ah, yes, yes," said Delancey, "but the adventures they have!"

"What adventures!"

"Look now, there was a sergeant in court only yesterday telling me about a miser, an old maid without a soul in the world that died in an ould loft on the quays. Well, this sergeant I'm talking about put a new man on duty outside the door while he went back to report, and all this fellow had to do was to kick the door and frighten off the rats."

"That's enough, that's enough!" cried Foley.

"Yes, yes, but listen now, listen can't you? He was there about ten minutes with a bit of a candle in his hand and all at once the door at the foot of the stairs began to open. 'Who's there?' says he, giving a start. 'Who's there I say?' There was no answer and still the door kept opening quietly. Then he gave a laugh. What was it but a cat? 'Puss, puss,' says he, 'come on up, puss!' Thinking, you know, the ould cat would be company. Up comes the cat, pitter-patter on the stairs, and then whatever look he gave the door the hair stood up on his head. What was coming in but another cat? 'Coosh!' says he, stamping his foot and kicking the door to frighten them. 'Coosh away to hell out of that!' And then another cat came in and then another, and in his fright he dropped the candle and kicked out right and left. The cats began to hiss and bawl, and that robbed him of the last stitch of sense. He bolted down the stairs, and as he did he trod on one of the brutes, and before he knew where he was he slipped and fell head over heels, and when he put out his hand to grip something 'twas a cat he gripped, and he felt the claws tearing his hands and face. He had strength enough to pull himself up and run, but when he reached the barrack gate down he dropped in a fit. He was a raving lunatic for three weeks after."

"And that," said Foley with bitter restraint, "is what you call adventure!"

"Dear knows," added Magner, drawing himself up with a shiver, "'tis a great consolation to be able to put on your cap and go out for a drink any hour of the night you like."

"'Tis of course," drawled Foley scornfully. "And to know the worst case you'll have in ten years is a bit of a scrap about politics."

"I dunno," sighed Delancey dreamily. "I'm telling you there's great charm about the Criminal Courts."

"Damn the much charm they had for you when you were in the box," growled Foley.

"I know, sure, I know," admitted Delancey, crestfallen.

"Shutting his eyes," said Magner with a laugh, "like a kid afraid he was going to get a box across the ears."

"And still," said Delancey, "this sergeant fellow I'm talking about, he said, after a while you wouldn't mind it no more than if 'twas a card party, but talk up to the judge himself."

"I suppose you would," agreed Magner pensively.

There was silence in the smoky compartment that jolted and rocked its way across Ireland, and the four occupants, each touched with that morning wit which afflicts no one so much as state witnesses, thought of how they would speak to the judge if only they had him before them now. They looked up to see a fat red face behind the door, and a moment later it was dragged back.

"Is thish my carriage, gentlemen?" asked a meek and boozy voice.

"No, 'tisn't. Go on with you!" snapped Magner.

"I had as nice a carriage as ever was put on a railway thrain," said the drunk, leaning in, "a handsome carriage, and 'tis losht."

"Try farther on," suggested Delancey.

"Excuse me interrupting yeer conversation, gentlemen."

"That's all right, that's all right."

"I'm very melancholic. Me besht friend, I parted him thish very night, and 'tish known to no wan, only the Almighty and Merciful God (here the drunk reverently raised his bowler hat and let it slide down the back of his neck to the floor), if I'll ever lay eyes on him agin in thish world. Good night, gentlemen, and thanks, thanks for all yeer kindness."

As the drunk slithered away up the corridor Delancey laughed. Fox resumed the conversation where it had left off.

"I'll admit," he said, "Delancey wasn't the only one."

"He was not," agreed Foley. "Even the sergeant was shook. When he caught up the mug he was trembling all over, and before he could let it down it danced a jig on the table."

"Ah, dear God! Dear God!" sighed Delancey, "what killed me most entirely was the bloody ould model of the house. I didn't mind anything else but the house. There it was, a living likeness, with the bit of grass in front and the shutter hanging loose, and every time I looked down I was in the back lane at Farranchreesht, hooshing the hens and smelling the turf, and then I'd look up and see the lean fellow in the wig pointing his finger at me."

"Well, thank God," said Foley with simple devotion, "this time tomorrow I'll be sitting in Ned Ivers' back with a pint in my fist."

Delancey shook his head, a dreamy smile playing upon his dark face.

"I dunno," he said. "'Tis a small place, Farranchreesht, a small, mangy ould *fothrach* of a place with no interest or advancement in it."

"There's something to be said on both sides," added Magner judicially. "I wouldn't say you're wrong, Foley, but I wouldn't say Delancey was wrong either."

"Here's the sergeant now," said Delancey, drawing himself up with a smile of welcome. "Ask him."

"He wasn't long getting tired of Julietta," whispered Magner maliciously.

The door was pushed back and the sergeant entered, loosening the collar of his tunic. He fell into a corner seat, crossed his legs and accepted the cigarette which Delancey proffered.

"Well, lads," he exclaimed. "What about a jorum!"

"By Gor," said Foley, "isn't it remarkable? I was only talking about it!"

"I have noted before now, Peter," said the sergeant, "that you and me have what might be called a simultaneous thirst."

3

The country folk were silent and exhausted. Kendillon drowsed now and again, but he suffered from blood pressure, and after a while his breathing grew thicker and stronger until at last it exploded in a snort, and then he started up, broad awake and angry. In the silence rain spluttered and tapped along the roof, and the dark window-panes streamed with shining runnels of water that trickled on to the floor. Moll Mor scowled, her lower lip thrust out. She was a great fop of a woman with a big coarse powerful face. The other two women, who kept their eyes closed, had their brown shawls drawn tight about their heads, but Moll's was round her shoulders and the gap above her breasts was filled by a blaze of scarlet.

"Where are we?" asked Kendillon crossly, starting awake after one of his drowsing fits.

Moll Mor glowered at him.

"Aren't we home yet?" he asked again.

"No," she answered. "Nor won't be. What scour is on you?"

"Me little house," moaned Kendillon.

"Me little house," mimicked Moll. " 'Twasn't enough for you to board the windows and put barbed wire on the ould bit of a gate!"

" 'Tis all dom well for you," he snarled, "that have someone to mind yours for you."

One of the women laughed softly and turned a haggard and virginal face within the cowl of her shawl.

" 'Tis that same have me laughing," she explained apologetically. "Tim Dwyer this week past at the stirabout pot!"

"And making the beds!" chimed in the third woman.

"And washing the children's faces! Glory be to God, he'll blast creation!"

"Ay," snorted Moll, "and his chickens running off with Thade Kendillon's roof."

"My roof, is it?"

"Ay, your roof."

" 'Tis a good roof. 'Tis a better roof than ever was seen over your head since the day you married."

"Oh, Mary Mother!" sighed Moll, " 'tis a great pity of me this three hours and I looking at the likes of you instead of me own fine bouncing man."

" 'Tis a new thing to hear you praising your man, then," said a woman.

"I wronged him," said Moll contritely. "I did so. I wronged him before the world."

At this moment the drunken man pulled back the door of the compartment and looked from face to face with an expression of deepening melancholy.

"She'sh not here," he said in disappointment.

"Who's not here, mister?" asked Moll with a wink at the others.

"I'm looking for me own carriage, ma'am," said the drunk with melancholy dignity, "and whatever the bloody hell they done with it, 'tish losht. The railways in thish country are gone to hell."

"Wisha, if 'tis nothing else is worrying you wouldn't you sit here with me?" asked Moll.

"I would with very great pleasure," replied the drunk, "but 'tishn't on'y the carriage, 'tish me thravelling companion. ...

I'm a lonely man, I parted me besht friend this very night, I found wan to console me, and then when I turned me back — God took her!"

And with a dramatic gesture the drunk closed the door and continued on his way. The country folk sat up, blinking. The smoke of the men's pipes filled the compartment, and the heavy air was laden with the smell of homespun and turf smoke, the sweet pungent odour of which had penetrated every fibre of their garments.

"Listen to the rain, leave ye!" said one of the women. "We'll have a wet walk home."

" 'Twill be midnight before we're there," said another.

"Ah, sure, the whole country will be up."

" 'Twill be like daylight with collogueing."

"There'll be no sleep in Farranchreesht tonight."

"Oh, Farranchreesht! Farranchreesht!" cried the young woman
with the haggard face, the ravished lineaments of which were suddenly
transfigured. "Farranchreesht and the sky over you, I wouldn't
change places with the Queen of England this night!"

And suddenly Farranchreesht, the bare boglands with the hump-
backed mountain behind, the little white houses and the dark forti-
fications of turf that made it seem the flame-blackened ruin of some
mighty city, all was lit up within their minds. An old man sitting in a
corner, smoking a broken clay pipe, thumped his stick upon the floor.

"Well, now," said Kendillon darkly, "wasn't it great impudence in
her to come back?"

"Wasn't it now?" answered a woman.

"She won't be there long," he added.

"You'll give her the hunt, I suppose?" asked Moll Mor politely, too
politely.

"If no one else do, I'll give her the hunt myself."

"Oh, the hunt, the hunt," agreed a woman. "No one could ever
darken her door again."

"And still, Thade Kendillon," pursued Moll with her teeth on edge
to be at him, "you swore black was white to save her neck."

"I did of course. What else would I do?"

"What else? What else, indeed?" agreed the others.

"There was never an informer in my family."

"I'm surprised to hear it," replied Moll vindictively, but the old man
thumped his stick three or four times on the floor requesting silence.

"We told our story, the lot of us," he said, "and we told it well."

"We did, indeed."

"And no one told it better than Moll Mor. You'd think to hear her
she believed it herself."

"God knows," answered Moll with a wild laugh, "I nearly did."

"And still I see great changes in my time, and maybe the day will
come when Moll Mor or her likes will have a different story."

A silence followed his words. There was profound respect in all
their eyes. The old man coughed and spat.

"Did any of ye ever think the day would come when a woman in our parish would do the like of that?"

"Never, never, ambasa!"

"But she might do it for land?"

"She might then."

"Or for money?"

"She might so."

"She might indeed. When the hunger is money people kill for money, when the hunger is land people kill for land. There's a great change coming, a great change. In the ease of the world people are asking more. When I was a growing boy in the barony if you killed a beast you made six pieces of it, one for yourself and the rest for neighbours. The same if you made a catch of fish, and that's how it was with us from the beginning of time. And now look at the change! The people aren't as poor as they were, nor as good as they were, nor as generous as they were, nor as strong as they were."

"Nor as wild as they were," added Moll Mor with a vicious glare at Kendillon. "Oh, glory be to You, God, isn't the world a wonderful place!"

The door opened and Magner, Delancey and the sergeant entered. Magner was drunk.

"Moll," he said, "I was lonely without you. You're the biggest and brazenest and cleverest liar of the lot and you lost me my sergeant's stripes, but I'll forgive you everything if you'll give us one bar of the 'Colleen Dhas Roo.' "

4

"I'm a lonely man," said the drunk. "And now I'm going back to my lonely habitation."

"Me besht friend," he continued, "I left behind me — Michael O'Leary. 'Tis a great pity you don't know Michael, and a great pity Michael don't know you. But look now at the misfortunate way a thing will happen. I was looking for someone to console me, and the moment I turned me back you were gone."

Solemnly he placed his hand under the woman's chin and raised her face to the light. Then with the other hand he stroked her cheeks.

"You have a beauful face," he said, "a beauful face. But whass more important, you have a beauful soul. I look into your eyes and I see the beauty of your nature. Allow me wan favour. Only wan favour before we part."

He bent and kissed her. Then he picked up his bowler which had fallen once more, put it on back to front, took his dispatch case and got out.

The woman sat on alone. Her shawl was thrown open and beneath it she wore a bright blue blouse. The carriage was cold, the night outside black and cheerless, and within her something had begun to contract that threatened to crush the very spark of life. She could no longer fight it off, even when for the hundredth time she went over the scenes of the previous day; the endless hours in the dock; the wearisome speeches and questions she couldn't understand and the long wait in the cells till the jury returned. She felt it again, the shiver of mortal anguish that went through her when the chief warder beckoned angrily from the stairs, and the wardress, glancing hastily into a hand-mirror, pushed her forward. She saw the jury with their expression-less faces. She was standing there alone, in nervous twitches jerking back the shawl from her face to give herself air. She was trying to say a prayer, but the words were being drowned within her mind by the thunder of nerves, crashing and bursting. She could feel one that had escaped dancing madly at the side of her mouth but she was power-less to recapture it.

"The verdict of the jury is that Helena Maguire is not guilty." Which was it? Death or life? She couldn't say. "Silence! Silence!" shouted the usher, though no one had tried to say anything. "Any other charge?" asked a weary voice. "Release the prisoner." "Silence!" shouted the crier again. The chief warder opened the door of the dock and she began to run. When she reached the steps she stopped and looked back to see if she were being followed. A policeman held open a door and she found herself in an ill-lit, draughty, stone corridor. She stood there, the old shawl about her face. The crowd began to emerge. The first was a tall girl with a wrapt expression as though she were walking on air. When she saw the woman she halted suddenly, her hands went up in an instinctive gesture, as though she wished to feel her, to caress her. It was that look of hers, that gait as of a sleep-walker that brought the woman back to her senses ...

But now the memory had no warmth in her mind, and the something within her continued to contract, smothering her with loneliness and shame and fear. She began to mutter crazily to herself. The train, now almost empty, was stopping at every little wayside station. Now and again a blast of wind from the Atlantic pushed at it as though trying to capsize it.

She looked up as the door was slammed open and Moll Mor came in, swinging her shawl behind her.

"They're all up the train. Wouldn't you come?"

"No, no, no, I couldn't."

"Why couldn't you? Who are you minding? Is it Thade Kendillon?"

"No, no, I'll stop as I am."

"Here! Take a sup of this and 'twill put new heart in you." Moll fumbled in her shawl and produced a bottle of liquor as pale as water. "Wait till I tell you what Magner said! That fellow's a limb of the divil. 'Have you e'er a drop, Moll?' says he. 'Maybe I have then,' says I. 'What is it?' says he. 'What do you think?' says I. 'For God's sake,' says he, 'baptize it quick and call it whiskey.'"

The woman took the bottle and put it to her lips. She shivered as she drank.

"'Tis powerful stuff entirely," said Moll with respect.

Next moment there were loud voices in the corridor. Moll grabbed the bottle and hid it under her shawl. The door opened and in strode Magner, and behind him the sergeant and Delancey, looking rather foolish. After them again came the two country women, giggling. Magner held out his hand.

"Helena," he said, "accept my congratulations."

The woman took his hand, smiling awkwardly.

"We'll get you the next time though," he added.

"Musha, what are you saying, mister?" she asked.

"Not a word, not a word. You're a clever woman, a remarkable woman, and I give you full credit for it. You threw dust in all our eyes."

"Poison," said the sergeant by way of no harm, "is hard to come by and easy to trace, but it beat me to trace it."

"Well, well, there's things they're saying about me!"

The woman laughed nervously, looking first at Moll Mor and then at the sergeant.

"Oh, you're safe now," said Magner, "as safe as the judge on the bench. Last night when the jury came out with the verdict you could have stood there in the dock and said, 'Ye're wrong, ye're wrong, I did it. I got the stuff in such and such a place. I gave it to him because he was old and dirty and cantankerous and a miser. I did it and I'm proud of it!' You could have said every word of that and no one would have dared to lay a finger on you."

"Indeed! What a thing I'd say!"

"Well you could."

"The law is truly a remarkable phenomenon," said the sergeant, who was also rather squiffy. "Here you are, sitting at your ease at the expense of the State, and for one word, one simple word of a couple of letters, you could be lying in the body of the gaol, waiting for the rope and the morning jaunt."

The woman shuddered. The young woman with the ravished face looked up.

" 'Twas the holy will of God," she said simply.

" 'Twas all the bloody lies Moll Mor told," replied Magner.

" 'Twas the will of God," she repeated.

"There was many hanged in the wrong," said the sergeant.

"Even so, even so! 'Twas God's will."

"You have a new blouse," said the other woman in an envious tone.

"I seen it last night in a shop on the quay," replied the woman with sudden brightness. "A shop on the way down from the court. Is it nice?"

"How much did it cost you?"

"Honour of God!" exclaimed Magner, looking at them in stupefaction. "Is that all you were thinking of? You should have been on your bended knees before the altar."

"I was too," she answered indignantly.

"Women!" exclaimed Magner with a gesture of despair. He winked at Moll Mor and the pair of them retired to the next compartment. But the interior was reflected clearly in the corridor window and they could see the pale, quivering image of the policeman lift Moll Mor's bottle to his lips and blow a long silent blast on it as on a trumpet. Delancey laughed.

"There'll be one good day's work done on the head of the trial," said the young woman, laughing.

"How so?" asked the sergeant.

"Dan Canty will make a great brew of poteen while he have yeer backs turned."

"I'll get Dan Canty yet," replied the sergeant stiffly.

"You will, as you got Helena."

"I'll get him yet."

He consulted his watch.

"We'll be in in another quarter of an hour," he said. " 'Tis time we were all getting back to our respective compartments."

Magner entered and the other policemen rose. The sergeant fastened his collar and buckled his belt. Magner swayed, holding the door frame, a mawkish smile on his thin, handsome, dissipated face.

"Well, good night to you now, ma'am," said the sergeant, primly. "I'm as glad for all our sakes things ended up as they did."

"Good night, Helena," said Magner, bowing low and promptly tottering. "There'll be one happy man in Farranchreesht tonight."

"Come! Come, Joe!" protested the sergeant.

"One happy man," repeated Magner obstinately. " 'Tis his turn now."

"Come on back, man," said Delancey. "You're drunk."

"You wanted him," said Magner heavily. "Your people wouldn't let you have him, but you have him at last in spite of them all."

"Do you mean Cady Driscoll?" hissed the woman with sudden anger, leaning towards Magner, the shawl drawn tight about her head.

"Never mind who I mean. You have him."

"He's no more to me now than the salt sea!"

The policeman went out first, the women followed, Moll Mor laughing boisterously. The woman was left alone. Through the window she could see little cottages stepping down through wet and naked rocks to the water's edge. The flame of life had narrowed in her to a pin-point, and she could only wonder at the force that had caught her up, mastered her and thrown her aside.

"No more to me," she repeated dully to her own image in the window, "no more to me than the salt sea!"

COMMENTARY

By contrast with the stark and single-minded economy of, say, *Be This Her Memorial,* O'Connor's story gives an immediate impression of spread, of the creation of an entire little world in rich, complex, and apparently sprawling detail. (You might note how many *kinds* of detail there are, and how they are interwoven to suggest the randomness of normal experience.) But to read this as journalism, or a slice of life, would be to miss its point altogether. Its appearance of casual spontaneity hides artifice of singular cunning, contrived not to diffuse concern but to concentrate and enrich it; and a feature of the narrative method is that it necessitates a high degree of alertness to the subtle adjustments by which this focus is slowly sharpened. Even a skilled reader, sensitive to technical subtlety, is likely to find a second or third reading unusually rewarding; though not primarily because he comes nearer disentangling an involved action, or as in a detective story, picks up more clues to the solution of a problem. (Can you call to mind any stories which offer the pleasure of a puzzle, and require an appropriate skill in the reading?) Here the opportunity of that sort of interest exists but has been pointedly refused. It would seem that O'Connor is not finally concerned with externals — that his hidden mechanism is not directed to a mechanical end but to the pointing of something human, and inward. And as always, the author's motive controls his choice, tone, and form.

O'Connor's choice of situation is curious. The material he is handling is potentially rich: it suggests a long sequence of events, past and to come, with many moments in it more obviously important and dramatic than the one he has selected. Indeed, in the normal way, this one would hardly be considered fruitful at all, or it would go unnoticed. (Consider the possibilities from the beginning of the sequence to the end — the initial situation, the motive and the crime; the investigation; the trial; the woman's return to the village and life there; the shadow of these events upon later ones. Name some notable authors who might have selected one or other of these to treat. Which choice would show a prime concern with the purely anecdotal potentialities of the story? with the dramatic? the melodramatic? the psychological? the moral? the tragic? the pathetic? the metaphysical? You might even try yourself to turn one or more of these episodes into a story.) The choice of characters is little more obvious. Of the various possible participants in the sequence some of the chief are hardly hinted at, whereas we get a searching look at the sergeant's wife, the police, and the villagers, most of whom are peripheral at best, and pointedly recurrent glimpses of adventitious travellers like the drunk and the young woman. *Why* the odious wife, Delancey, Moll Mor, Kendillon, the old man, and the rest? Finally there is the choice of action. What O'Connor gives us is not at all a spectacular anecdote, as it could easily have been. One might reasonably ask what in fact does happen in the story.

Another interesting peculiarity of the piece is its duality of tone. One shifts throughout between the bizarre and boozy drollery of the dialogues and incidents, and the grave detachment, even heavy inevitability, of O'Connor's narrative manner. But there are two moments when the roaring farce itself is suddenly interrupted — at the old man's speech, and at the woman's outburst. The effect of the abrupt change is dramatic emphasis: the two declarations are given climactic force, and thus isolated, are thrown into pointed parallel. (Your task of course is to ponder the implications of the effects gained by these manipulations of tone. What is conveyed to the reader, albeit tacitly, about the way O'Connor wants him to view the events and the people? What complications, or complexities, are suggested by the contrasts and the parallels? These are questions to come back on when you have already got a good deal out of the story.) One further point to remark here is evident enough in the piece, and that is the high imaginative pressure under which it was written. This does not mean that its emotional temperature is high — for the most part feeling is notably restrained. But the entire situation has been conceived and felt with a quite uncommon intensity, which charges the overall design and shows through the texture of the narrative in a compelling vividness of invention, visualization, and speech. One notes among much else the storm-lashed train in the void of Ireland at night, the contrasted little worlds of the compartments, the scene at the station, the sharp vision of Farranchreesht and the fervent outburst of the young woman in praise of the place, the interventions of the drunk (and particularly his scene with the woman), the flashes of the alien prospect outside, culminating in the final tableau of sea-edge cottages, the poetic pungency of the reiterated last speech. Undoubtedly such effects give colour, and some of them carry emotional charge. But one looks for more than that. Can it be said that they are organically related to the central development of the story? (Bear in mind that literary effect, which is bound up with imagination and feeling as well as with verbal concepts, is not necessarily confined to what can be fully rationalized in words.)

We come back to the question of what actually happens. And this is closely connected with form; which, in its turn, is determined by the overall device of the train journey (remember O'Connor's praise of Chekhov). In a number of ways, that device is conspicuously successful. It fixes a term, the limits of the journey itself; it provides a multiple location, which is at once homogeneous, fluid, and dramatically dense; above all, it presents us with a little world, an exact microcosm of the society outside it. Development comes simply by way of a passage from one compartment of the train to another, with a little complication from the intermingling of the groups: four conversations, increasing in weight, *and converging*. These conversations are closely interrelated. They show a steady concentration, and a steady, but very oblique, disclosure; and by these we move slowly to the centre of the story. The concentration is on the travellers' destination and home, Farranchreesht. The disclosure is that seemingly spontaneous discovery of the whole circumstances of the journey. Both involve parallel expression of attitudes from the groups, and there is a good deal of irony in the way these attitudes contrast. (Incidental irony? Look for such contrasts, and see whether they carry implicit comment on the characters of the people involved — on the sergeant's wife, for example. They may also tell you where O'Connor's sympathies lie, and what he values in people — a paradoxical esteem in this case, perhaps. What, moreover, might be the main reason for the concentration on Farranchreesht?)

A last contrast to note, greatly effective but also functional, is that between the chattering compartments and the silent immobility of the woman when at length we reach her. The whole movement of the story leads us to expect a significant breaking of that silence, or a final inner disclosure. We get both; but they are probably not what we expected. Nothing is said of guilt, or blame, conscience, or triumph, and motive is only hinted at to fire the culminating outburst. What is revealed is a state of feeling, unaccountable, incomprehensible to the woman herself, and presented without any discussion or analysis. The centre of the story is simply the uncovering of an emotional truth, with the implied comment, "This, inexplicable and strange as it may be, is the way life works."

8

H. E. BATES

1905-

H. E. BATES (educated at Kettering Grammar School) has the distinction of having appeared more often than any other writer in E. J. O'Brien's annual *Best British Short Stories*. Although he has written novels and plays, it is as a writer of short stories that Bates is known. In this field there are few who write with such virtuosity. Economy of expression and sensitivity to atmosphere are his prime virtues. To these are allied a descriptive skill and the ability to create moments of intense emotion. Every writer of worth has his own approach to his task and Bates has no ready-made formula for the short story, but it can be seen that he favours a situation that involves persons drawn from the world of common folk, brought to a moment of heightened experience.

Perhaps this fondness for country life and characters owes something to his origin in that part of the Midlands that is at least as much rural as industrial and to his grandfather's reminiscences of gipsies and prize-fighters. These anecdotes Bates heard whilst a young man, already more interested in learning about people than in pursuing the humdrum course of a clerk in a local leather factory. Bates was fortunate in engaging the sympathetic interest of Edward Garnett and his son, David Garnett, when he began to write. Although, like many a young writer, Bates was influenced by contemporary masters, it was not long before he found his own matter and his own manner. These can be comprehensively summed up as "thoroughly English".

His steady success led to his being the first short story writer commissioned by the British Government to write about the R.A.F. and to his being sent to Burma to cover operations there.

It is not surprising that one who has been so expert a practitioner himself should examine critically his own medium. This Bates has done in *The Modern Short Story: A Critical Survey* (1950). In his first chapter, "Retrospect", he establishes the fact that there is no categorical imperative for the short story — "The basis of almost every argument or conclusion I can make is the axiom that the short story can be anything that the author decides it shall be." He adds, developing a dictum of E. J. O'Brien, that what matters in short stories is "the measure of how vitally compelling the writer makes his selected facts or incidents" and sums up the Protean nature of short stories thus: "There is no definition, no measure, which will aptly contain the structure, effect, and beauty of them all."

Suggested reading: *Colonel Julian and other Stories* (1956); *Cut and Come Again* (1955); *Fair Stood the Wind for France* (1949); *Love for Lydia* (1952); *My Uncle Silas* (1953); *Stories of Flying Officer 'X'* (1952); *The Purple Plain* (1951); *The Scarlet Sword* (1956); *Thirty-one Selected Tales* (1951); *Twenty Tales* (1951); and many more.

*   *   *

The Mower

IN the midday heat of a June day a farm-boy was riding down a deserted meadow-lane, straddling a fat white pony. The blossoms of hawthorn had shrivelled to brown on the tall hedges flanking the lane and wild pink and white roses were beginning to open like stars among the thick green leaves. The air was heavy with the scent of early summer, the odour of the dying hawthorn bloom, the perfume of the dog-roses, the breath of ripening grass.

The boy had taken off his jacket and had hooked it over the straw victual-bag hanging from the saddle. There were bottles of beer in the bag and the jacket shaded them from the heat of the sun. The pony moved at walking-pace and the boy rode cautiously, never letting it break into a trot. As though it was necessary to be careful with the beer, he sometimes halted the pony and touched the necks of the bottles with his fingers. The bottle-necks were cool, but the cloth of his jacket was burning against his hand.

He presently steered the pony through a white gate leading from the lane to a meadow beyond. The gate was standing open and he rode the pony straight across the curving swathes of hay which lay drying in the sun. It was a field of seven or eight acres and a third of the grass had already been mown. The hay was crisp and dry under the pony's feet and the flowers that had been growing in the grass lay white and shrivelled in the sunshine.

Over on the far side of the field a man was mowing, and a woman was turning the rows of grass with a hay-rake. The figure of the man was nondescript and dark, and the woman was dressed in a white blouse and an old green skirt that had faded to the yellowish colour of the grass the man was mowing. The boy rode the pony towards them. The sunshine blazed down fierce and perpendicular, and there was no shade in the field except for the shadow of an ash tree in one corner and a group of willows by a cattle-pond in another.

Everywhere was silence and the soft sound of the pony's feet in the hay and the droning of bees in the flowers among the uncut grass seemed to deepen the silence.

The woman straightened her back and, leaning on her rake, shaded her face with her hand and looked across at the boy as she heard him coming. The man went on mowing, swinging the scythe slowly and methodically, his back towards her.

The woman was dark and good-looking, with a sleek swarthy face and very high, soft red cheek-bones, like a gipsy, and a long pigtail of thick black hair which she wore twisted over her head like a snake coiled up asleep. She herself was rather like a snake also, her long body slim and supple, her black eyes liquid and bright. The boy rode up to her and dismounted. She dropped her rake and held the pony's head and ran her fingers up and down its nose while he slipped from the saddle.

"Can he come?" she said.

The boy had not time to answer before the man approached, wiping the sweat from his face and neck with a dirty red hand-kerchief.

His face was broad and thick-lipped and ponderous, his eyes were grey and simple, and the skin of his face and neck and hands was dried and tawny as an Indian's with sun and weather. He was about forty, and he walked with a slight stoop of his shoulders and a limp of his left leg, very slowly and deliberately.

"See him?" he said to the boy.

"He was up there when I got the beer," the boy said.

"In the Dragon? What did he say?"

"He said he'd come."

The woman ceased stroking the pony's nose and looked up.

"He said that yesterday," she said.

"Ah! but you can't talk to him. He's got to have his own way," said the man. "Was he drunk?" he asked.

"I don't think so," said the boy. "He was drunk yesterday."

The man wiped his neck impatiently and made a sound of disgust and then took out his watch. "Half the day gone — and a damn wonder if he comes," he muttered.

"Oh! if Ponto says he'll come," said the woman slowly, "he'll come. He'll come all right."

"How do you know? He does things just when he thinks he will — and not until."

"Oh! He'll come if he says he'll come," she said.

The boy began to lead the pony across the field towards the ash tree. The woman stood aside for him and then kicked her rake on a heap of hay and followed him.

The sun had crossed the zenith. The man went back to his scythe and slipped his whetstone from his pocket and laid it carefully on the mown grass. As he put on his jacket he turned and gazed at the white gate of the field. He could see no one there, and he followed the woman and the boy across the field to the ash tree.

Under the ash tree the boy was tethering the horse in the shade and the woman was unpacking bread and cold potatoes and a meat pie. The boy had finished tethering the horse as the man came up and he was covering over the bottles of beer with a heap of hay. The sight of the beer reminded the man of something.

"You told him the beer was for him?" he asked.

"He asked me whose it was and I told him what you said," the boy replied.

"That's all right."

He began to unfold the sack in which the blade of his scythe had been wrapped. He spread out the sack slowly and carefully on the grass at the foot of the ash trunk and let his squat body sink down upon it heavily. The boy and the woman seated themselves on the grass at his side. He unhooked the heavy soldier's knife hanging from his belt, and unclasped it and wiped it on his trousers knee. The woman sliced the pie. The man took his plateful of pie and bread and potatoes on his knee, and spitting his suckle-pebble from his mouth began spearing the food with the point of his knife, eating ravenously. When he did not eat with his knife he ate with his fingers, grunting and belching happily. The woman finished serving the pie, and sucking a smear of gravy from her long fingers, began to eat too.

During the eating no one spoke. The three people stared at the half-mown field. The curves of the scythed grass were beginning to whiten in the blazing sunshine. The heat shimmered and danced above the earth in the distance in little waves.

Before long the man wiped his plate with a piece of bread and swilled down his food with long drinks of cold tea from a blue can. When he had finished drinking, his head lolled back against the ash tree and he closed his eyes. The boy lay flat on his belly, reading a sporting paper while he ate. The air was stifling and warm even under the ash tree, and there was no sound in the noon stillness, except the clink of the horse's bit as it pulled off the young green leaves of the hawthorn hedge.

But suddenly the woman sat up a little and the drowsy look on her face began to clear away. A figure of a man had appeared at the white gate and was walking across the field. He walked with a kind of swaggering uncertainty and now and then he stopped and took up a handful of mown grass and dropped it again. He was carrying a scythe on his shoulder.

She watched him intently as he skirted the standing grass and came towards the ash tree. He halted at last within the shade of the tree and took a long look at the expanse of grass, thick with buttercups and tall bull-daisies, scattered everywhere like a white and yellow mass of stars.

"By Christ!" he muttered softly.

His voice was jocular and tipsy. The woman stood up.

"What's the matter, Ponto?" she said.

"This all he's cut?"

"That's all."

"By Christ."

He laid his scythe on the grass in disgust. He was a tall, thin, black-haired fellow, about thirty, lean and supple as a stoat; his sharp, dark-brown eyes were filled with a roving expression, half dissolute and half cunning; the light in them was sombre with drinking. His soft red lips were full and pouting, and there was something about his face altogether conceited, easy-going and devilish. He had a curious habit of looking at things with one eye half closed in a kind of sleepy wink that was marvellously knowing and attractive. He was wearing a dark slouch hat which he had tilted back from his forehead and which gave him an air of being a little wild but sublimely happy.

Suddenly he grinned at the woman and walked over to where the man lay sleeping. He bent down and put his mouth close to his face.

"Hey, your old hoss's bolted!" he shouted.

The man woke with a start.

"Your old hoss's bolted!"

"What's that? Where did you spring from?"

"Get up, y' old sleepy guts. I wanna get this grass knocked down afore dark."

The man got to his feet.

"Knock this lot down afore dark?"

"Yes, my old beauty. When I mow I do mow, I do." He smiled and wagged his head. "Me and my old dad used to mow twenty-acre fields afore dark — and start with the dew on. Twenty-acre fields. You don't know what mowin' is."

He began to take off his jacket. He was slightly unsteady on his feet and the jacket bothered him as he pulled it off, and he swore softly. He was wearing a blue-and-white shirt and a pair of dark moleskin trousers held up by a wide belt of plaited leather thongs. His whetstone rested in a leather socket hanging from the belt. He spat on his hands and slipped the whetstone from the socket and picked up his scythe and with easy, careless rhythmical swings began to whet the long blade. The woman gazed at the stroke of his arm and listened to the sharp ring of the stone against the blade with a look of unconscious admiration and pleasure on her face. The blade of the scythe was very long, tapering and slender, and it shone like silver in the freckles of sunlight coming through the ash leaves. He ceased sharpening the blade and took a swing at a tuft of bull-daisies. The blade cut the stalks crisply and the white flowers fell evenly together, like a fallen nosegay. His swing was beautiful and with the scythe in his hand the balance of his body seemed to become perfect and he himself suddenly sober, dignified, and composed.

"Know what my old dad used to say?" he said.

"No."

"Drink afore you start."

"Fetch a bottle of beer for Ponto," said the man to the boy at once. "I got plenty of beer." The boy went up on the way and fetched it.

"That's a good job. You can't mow without beer."

"That's right."

"My old man used to drink twenty pints a day. God's truth. Twenty pints a day. He was a bloody champion. You can't mow without beer."

The woman came up with a bottle of beer in her hand. Ponto took it from her mechanically, hardly looking at her. He uncorked the bottle, covered the white froth with his mouth and drank eagerly, the muscles of his neck rippling like those of a horse. He drank all the beer at one draught and threw the empty bottle into the hedge, scaring the pony.

"Whoa! damn you!" he shouted.

The pony tossed his head and quietened again. Ponto wiped his lips, and taking a step or two towards the boy, aimed the point of the scythe jocularly at his backside. The boy ran off and Ponto grinned tipsily at the woman.

"You goin' to turn the rows?" he said.

"Yes," she said.

He looked her up and down, from the arch of her hips to the clear shape of her breasts in her blouse and the coil of her black pigtail. Her husband was walking across the field to fetch his scythe. She smiled drowsily at Ponto and he smiled in return.

"I thought you'd come," she said softly.

His smile broadened and he stretched his hand and let his fingers run down her bare brown throat. She quivered and breathed quickly and laughed softly in return. His eyes rested on her face with mysterious admiration and delight and he seemed suddenly very pleased about something.

"Good old Anna," he said softly.

He walked past her and crossed the field to the expanse of unmown grass. He winked solemnly and his fingers ran lightly against her thigh as he passed her.

The woman followed him out into the sunshine and took up her rake and began to turn the rows that had been cut since early morning. When she glanced up again the men were mowing. They seemed to be mowing at the same even, methodical pace, but Ponto was already ahead. He swung his scythe with a long light caressing sweep, smoothly and masterfully, as though his limbs had been born to mow. The grass was shaved off very close to the earth and was laid behind him like a thick rope. On the backward stroke the grass and the buttercups and the bull-daisies were pressed gently backwards, bent in readiness to meet the forward swing that came through the grass with a soft swishing sound like the sound of indrawn breath.

The boy came and raked in the row next to the woman. Together they turned the rows and the men mowed in silence for a long time. Every time the woman looked up she looked at Ponto. He was always ahead of her husband, and he mowed with a kind of lusty insistence, as though he were intent on mowing the whole field before darkness fell. Her husband mowed in a stiff, awkward fashion, always limping and often whetting his scythe. The boy had taken some beer to Ponto, who often stopped to drink. She would catch the flash of the bottle tilted up in the brilliant sunshine and she would look at him meditatively as though remembering something.

As the afternoon went on, Ponto mowed far ahead of her husband, working across the field towards the pond and the willows. He began at last to mow a narrow space behind the pond. She saw the swing of his bare arms through the branches and then lost them again.

Suddenly he appeared and waved a bottle and shouted something.

"I'll go," she said to the boy.

She dropped her rake and walked over to the ash tree and found a bottle of beer. The flies were tormenting the horse and she broke off an ash bough and slipped it in the bridle. The sun seemed hotter than ever as she crossed the field with the beer, and the earth was cracked and dry under her feet. She picked up a stalk of buttercups and swung it against her skirt. The scent of the freshly mown grass was strong and sweet in the sunshine. She carried the beer close to her side, in the shadow.

Ponto was mowing a stretch of grass thirty or forty yards wide behind the pond. The grass was richer and taller than in the rest of the field and the single swathes he had cut lay as thick as corn.

She sat down on the bank of the pond under a willow until he had finished his bout of mowing. She had come up silently, and he was mowing with his back towards her, and it was not until he turned that he knew she was there.

He laid his scythe in the grass and came sidling up to her. His face was drenched in sweat and in his mouth was a stalk of totter-grass and the dark red seeds trembled as he walked.

"Good old Anna," he said.

"You did want beer?" she said.

He smiled and sat down at her side.

She too smiled with a flash of her black eyes. He took the bottle from her hand and put one hand on her knee and caressed it gently. She watched the hand with a smile of strange, wicked, ironical amusement. He put the bottle between his knees and unscrewed the stopper.

"Drink," he said softly.

She drank and gave him the bottle.

"Haven't seen you for ages," she murmured.

He shrugged his shoulders and took a long drink. His hand was still on her knee and as she played idly with the stalk of buttercups, her dark face concealed its rising passion in a look of wonderful pre-occupation, as though she had forgotten him completely. He wetted his lips with his tongue and ran his hand swiftly and caressingly from her knees to her waist. Her body was stiff for one moment and then it relaxed and sank backwards into the long grass. She shut her eyes and slipped into his embrace like a snake, her face blissfully happy, her hand still clasping the stalk of buttercups, her whole body trembling.

Presently across the field came the sound of a scythe being sharpened. She whispered something quickly and struggled and Ponto got to his feet. She sat up and buttoned the neck of her blouse. She was flushed and panting, and her eyes rested on Ponto with a soft, almost beseeching look of adoration.

Ponto walked away to his scythe and picked it up and began mowing again. He mowed smoothly and with a sort of aloof indifference as though nothing had happened, and she let him mow for five or six paces before she too stood up.

"Ponto," she whispered.

"Eh?"

"I'll come back," she said.

She remained for a moment in an attitude of expectancy, but he did not speak or cease the swing of his arms, and very slowly she turned away and went back across the field.

She walked back to where she had left her rake. She picked up the rake and began to turn the swathes of hay again, following the boy. She worked for a long time without looking up. When at last she lifted her head and looked over towards the pond, she saw that Ponto had ceased mowing behind the pond and was cutting in the open field again. He was mowing with the same easy, powerful insistence and with the same beautiful swaggering rhythm of his body, as though he could never grow tired.

They worked steadily on and the sun began to swing round behind the ash tree and the heat to lessen and twilight began to fall. While the two men were mowing side by side on the last strip of grass, the woman began to pack the victual-bags and put the saddle on the horse under the ash tree.

She was strapping the girth of the saddle when she heard feet in the grass and a voice said softly:

"Any more beer?"

She turned and saw Ponto. A bottle of beer was left in the bag and she brought it out for him. He began drinking, and while he was drinking she gazed at him with rapt admiration, as though she had been mysteriously attracted out of herself by the sight of his subtle, conceited, devilish face, the memory of his embrace by the pond and the beautiful untiring motion of his arms swinging the scythe

I   129

throughout the afternoon. There was something altogether trustful, foolish and abandoned about her, as though she were sublimely eager to do whatever he asked.

"Think you'll finish?" she said in a whisper.

"Easy."

He corked the beer and they stood looking at each other. He looked at her with a kind of careless, condescending stare, half smiling. She stood perfectly still, her eyes filled with half-happy, half-frightened submissiveness.

He suddenly wiped the beer from his lips with the back of his hand and put out his arm and caught her waist and tried to kiss her.

"Not now," she said desperately. "Not now. He'll see. Afterwards. He'll see."

He gave her a sort of half-pitying smile and shrugged his shoulders and walked away across the field without a word.

"Afterwards," she called in a whisper.

She went on packing the victual-bags, the expression on her face lost and expectant. The outlines of the field and the figure of the mowers became softer and darker in the twilight. The evening air was warm and heavy with the scent of the hay.

The men ceased mowing at last. The boy had gone home and the woman led the horse across the field to where the men were waiting. Her husband was tying the sack about the blade of his scythe. She looked at Ponto with a dark, significant flash of her eyes, but he took no notice.

"You'd better finish the beer," she said.

He took the bottle and drank to the dregs and then hurled the bottle across the field. She tried to catch his eye, but he was already walking away over the field, as though he had never seen her.

She followed him with her husband and the horse. They came to the gate of the field and Ponto was waiting. A look of anticipation and joy shot up in her eyes.

"Why should I damn well walk?" said Ponto. "Eh? Why should I damn well walk up this lane when I can sit on your old hoss? Lemme get up."

He laid his scythe in the grass and while the woman held the horse he climbed into the saddle.

"Give us me scythe," he asked. "I can carry that. Whoa! mare, damn you!"

She picked up the scythe and gave it to him and he put it over his shoulder. She let her hand touch his knee and fixed her eyes on him with a look of inquiring eagerness, but he suddenly urged the horse forward and began to ride away up the lane.

She followed her husband out of the field. He shut the gate and looked back over the darkening field at the long swathes of hay lying pale yellow in the dusk. He seemed pleased and he called to Ponto:

"I don't know what the Hanover we should ha' done without you, Ponto."

Ponto waved his rein-hand with sublime conceit.

"That's nothing," he called back. "Me and my old dad used to mow forty-acre fields afore dark. God damn it, that's nothing. All in the day's work."

He seized the rein again and tugged it and the horse broke into a trot, Ponto bumping the saddle and swearing and shouting as he went up the lane.

The woman followed him with her husband. He walked slowly, limping, and now and then she walked on a few paces ahead, as though trying to catch up with the retreating horse. Sometimes the horse would come almost down into a walk and she would come almost to within speaking distance of Ponto, but each time the horse would break into a fresh trot and leave her as far behind again. The lane was dusky with twilight and Ponto burst into a song about a girl and a sailor.

"Hark at him," said the husband. "He's a Tartar. He's a Tartar."

The rollicking voice seemed to echo over the fields with soft, deliberate mocking. The woman did not speak: but as she listened her dark face was filled with the conflicting expression of many emotions, exasperation, perplexity, jealousy, longing, hope, anger.

COMMENTARY

Many readers or would-be readers of the short story are disconcerted, if not positively alienated, by a story that has little or no action. They have formed, probably quite early and almost certainly subconsciously, ideas about what a short story should be. From the reading of stories by, for example, Conan Doyle, O. Henry or Somerset Maugham, they come to form certain notions or expectations of what a short story should contain — a revelation of hidden fact (as in many detective stories), a rapidly developed action or complication, an arresting climax, followed quite often — and especially in O. Henry — by a twist in the ending. Excellent stories, indeed, have been written to this formula and you may find some stories in this collection which make use of some of the features just mentioned. But not *The Mower*. Here is a story which, if it can be said to belong to a recognized type, derives rather from Chekhov than from any of the expert practitioners referred to above. If this kind of story can be expressed in a phrase, it is "a moment of life".

It will, of course, be understood that the phrase so used is in no way an indication of all that the story conveys. No moment can be isolated from the context of life. It is, in fact, the creation of this context that is of critical importance. We must be made, within the restricted compass within which the writer must work, to feel completely absorbed into the world of the persons involved. The way of life habitually theirs must be so presented that we can move with them into the selected moment that becomes for them significant and memorable and which constitutes the "point" of the story. It is in the creation of this atmosphere, at once physical and spiritual (or psychological, if you prefer that word) that H. E. Bates excels.

Nothing could be, apparently, simpler than this story of Anna who gives herself to the black-haired Ponto. It is the art of Bates so to work upon us that we feel the inevitability of the surrender and the conflicting reactions of Anna. To do this he must first establish the appropriate atmosphere. From the first words of the story we sense the heat of this June day. (Study carefully the first paragraph and note how the burden of summer drowziness is emphasized. Observe the economy of writing by which only this essential languorousness is created as the ambience of the events to follow.) Once the pervasiveness of the heat, nicely counterpointed by the insistence on the need to press on with the labour of mowing, has been realized, you can the better understand how Anna is stimulated by expectation of Ponto's coming. (Here you may ask yourself by what means interest is aroused in a character who has yet to appear — cf. Shakespeare's Othello. Who first asks if Ponto can come? What do we know of him from the conversation of the husband and wife with the boy? Can we learn anything of the relations of Anna and her husband that may have relevance to Anna's remarks about Ponto?)

Once Ponto has come, every movement, every gesture, every word of his, is significant. In this way — by the cumulative effect of the trivial and the incidental — we are drawn on to the climax. (Many writers would treat this at greater length than does Bates: ask yourself why that would be an artistic flaw.) And here you should note how what may not have seemed of importance takes on significance: the beer, the shape of the field, the rate at which Ponto and the husband respectively work.

If it is necessary in the appreciation of the story to observe closely the behaviour of Anna up to the moment of her surrender, and equally important not to miss the control which Bates exercises in the culmination of Anna's infatuation, it is also a point of appreciation to see how Bates brings the story to its close. For one of the best features of this story is its perfect symmetry. (Note Anna's feelings as she waits for the coming of Ponto and the full implications of the final sentence.) There is in *The Mower* a perfect sense of proportion and this you can think out in relation to the passing of time, the rise and fall of the dramatic arch implicit in the sequence of events, the relative prominence of Anna and her husband (why has Bates not named him?).

What are the distinctive qualities of *The Mower*? The answer to this question may perhaps be found in following the line of critical thought suggested by this phrase — intensity of focus.

9

LIONEL TRILLING

1905-

DAVID DAICHES in an article on "The Mind of Lionel Trilling" (*Commentary*, July 1957) says that this famous critic is "my idea of the perfect New York intellectual." Apart from the qualities of scholarship and broadmindedness, of insight and judgment that may be expected of a man of Trilling's academic standing (since 1948 he has been Professor of English at Columbia University) Daiches's phrase reminds us that Lionel Trilling is not simply a scholar, but a scholar in a country where the national ethos and ambience are not wholly congenial to those liberal and cultural values for which Trilling stands and which he has championed both explicitly in his essays and implicitly in such stories as *Of This Time, Of That Place*.

He was born in New York City and after passing through the "public schools" (as the State schools are called) graduated from Columbia in 1925, proceeding M.A. the following year. He returned as Instructor to Columbia after a period first at the University of Wisconsin and then at Hunter College, New York. He began writing in 1925; stories, essays, and reviews have appeared in a wide variety of literary and academic publications. "He looks, and dresses, like almost any conservative, middle-aged businessman", writes a contributor to *The Saturday Review of Literature* (February 14th, 1948), "and he teaches English with the utmost respectability at Columbia University. Yet he stands as one of the most important figures among America's left-of-centre intellectuals." He is particularly noteworthy for his grounding of criticism upon a moral basis. His viewpoint may be discerned in such a comment as "there are moments in literature which do not yield the secret of their power to any study of language, because the power does not depend on language but on the moral imagination." As he concludes a penetrating article on "The Situation of the American Intellectual at the Present Time" (1952/1953), "the kind of critical interest I am asking the literary intellectual to take in the life around him is a proper interest of the literary mind, ... it is the right ground for the literary art to grow in — the right ground for satire, for humour, for irony, for tragedy, for the personal vision affirming itself against the institutional with the peculiar passionateness of art. Art, strange and sad as it may be to say it again, really is a criticism of life." His story *Of This Time, Of That Place* will be the more fully appreciated if these words are borne in mind.

Suggested Reading: *The Middle of the Journey* (1947); *The Liberal Imagination* (1950); *The Opposing Self* (1955); *A Gathering Of Fugitives* (1956).

*   *   *

Of This Time, Of That Place

I

IT was a fine September day. By noon it would be summer again but now it was true autumn with a touch of chill in the air. As Joseph Howe stood on the porch of the house in which he lodged, ready to leave for his first class of the year, he thought with pleasure of the long indoor days that were coming. It was a moment when he could feel glad of his profession.

On the lawn the peach tree was still in fruit and young Hilda Aiken was taking a picture of it. She held the camera tight against her her chest. She wanted the sun behind her but she did not want her own long morning shadow in the fore-ground. She raised the camera but that did not help, and she lowered it but that made things worse. She twisted her body to the left, then to the right. In the end she had to step out of the direct line of the sun. At last she snapped the shutter and wound the film with intense care.

Howe, watching her from the porch, waited for her to finish and called good morning. She turned, startled, and almost sullenly lowered her glance. In the year Howe had lived at the Aikens', Hilda had accepted him as one of her family, but since his absence of the summer she had grown shy. Then suddenly she lifted her head and smiled at him, and the humorous smile confirmed his pleasure in the day. She picked up her book-bag and set off for school.

The handsome houses on the streets to the college were not yet fully awake but they looked very friendly. Howe went by the Bradby house where he would be a guest this evening at the first dinner-party of the year. When he had gone the length of the picket fence, the whitest in town, he turned back. Along the path there was a fine row of asters and he went through the gate and picked one for his buttonhole. The Bradbys would be pleased if they happened to see him invading their lawn and the knowledge of this made him even more comfortable.

He reached the campus as the hour was striking. The students were hurrying to their classes. He himself was in no hurry. He stopped at his dim cubicle of an office and lit a cigarette. The prospect of facing his class had suddenly presented itself to him and his hands were cold, the lawful seizure of power he was about to make seemed momentous. Waiting did not help. He put out his cigarette, picked up a pad of theme paper and went to his classroom.

As he entered, the rattle of voices ceased and the twenty-odd freshmen settled themselves and looked at him appraisingly. Their faces seemed gross, his heart sank at their massed impassivity, but he spoke briskly.

"My name is Howe," he said and turned and wrote it on the blackboard. The carelessness of the scrawl confirmed his authority. He went on: "My office is 412 Slemp Hall and my office hours are Monday, Wednesday, and Friday from eleven-thirty to twelve-thirty."

He wrote: "M., W., F., 11.30-12.30." He said: "I'll be very glad to see any of you at that time. Or if you can't come then, you can arrange with me for some other time."

He turned again to the blackboard and spoke over his shoulder. "The text for the course is Jarman's *Modern Plays*, revised edition. The Co-op has it in stock." He wrote the name, underlined "revised edition" and waited for it to be taken down in the new note-books.

When the bent heads were raised again he began his speech of prospectus. "It is hard to explain — " he said, and paused as they composed themselves. "It is hard to explain what a course like this is intended to do. We are going to try to learn something about modern literature and something about prose composition."

As he spoke, his hands warmed and he was able to look directly at the class. Last year on the first day the faces had seemed just as cloddish, but as the term wore on they became gradually alive and quite likeable. It did not seem possible that the same thing could happen again.

"I shall not lecture in this course," he continued. "Our work will be carried on by discussion and we will try to learn by an exchange of opinion. But you will soon recognize that my opinion is worth more than anyone else's here."

He remained grave as he said it, but two boys understood and laughed. The rest took permission from them and laughed too. All Howe's private ironies protested the vulgarity of the joke but the laughter made him feel benign and powerful.

When the little speech was finished, Howe picked up the pad of paper he had brought. He announced that they would write an extemporaneous theme. Its subject was traditional: "Who I am and why I came to Dwight College." By now the class was more at ease and it gave a ritualistic groan of protest. Then there was a stir as fountain-pens were brought out and the writing arms of chairs were cleared and the paper was passed about. At last all the heads bent to work and the room became still.

Howe sat idly at his desk. The sun shone through the tall clumsy windows. The cool of the morning was already passing. There was a scent of autumn and of varnish, and the stillness of the room was deep and oddly touching. Now and then a student's head was raised and scratched in the old elaborate students' pantomime that calls the teacher to witness honest intellectual effort.

Suddenly a tall boy stood within the frame of the open door. "Is this," he said, and thrust a large nose into a college catalogue, "is this the meeting place of English 1A? The section instructed by Dr Joseph Howe?"

He stood on the very sill of the door, as if refusing to enter until he was perfectly sure of all his rights. The class looked up from work, found him absurd and gave a low mocking cheer.

The teacher and the new student, with equal pointedness, ignored the disturbance. Howe nodded to the boy, who pushed his head forward and then jerked it back in a wide elaborate arc to clear his brow of a heavy lock of hair. He advanced into the room and halted before Howe, almost at attention. In a loud clear voice he announced: "I am Tertan, Ferdinand R., reporting at the direction of Head of Department Vincent."

The heraldic formality of this statement brought forth another cheer. Howe looked at the class with a sternness he could not really feel, for there was indeed something ridiculous about this boy. Under his displeased regard the rows of heads dropped back to work again. Then he touched Tertan's elbow, led him up to the desk and stood so as to shield their conversation from the class.

"We are writing an extemporaneous theme," he said. "The subject is: 'Who I am and why I came to Dwight College'."

He stripped a few sheets from the pad and offered them to the boy. Tertan hesitated and then took the paper, but he held it only tentatively. As if with the effort of making something clear, he gulped, and a slow smile fixed itself on his face. It was at once knowing and shy.

"Professor," he said, "to be perfectly fair to my classmates" — he made a large gesture over the room — "and to you" — he inclined his head to Howe — "this would not be for me an extemporaneous subject."

Howe tried to understand. "You mean you've already thought about it — you've heard we always give the same subject? That doesn't matter."

Again the boy ducked his head and gulped. It was the gesture of one who wished to make a difficult explanation with perfect candour. "Sir," he said, and made the distinction with great care, "the topic I did not expect but I have given much ratiocination to the subject."

Howe smiled and said: "I don't think that's an unfair advantage. Just go ahead and write."

Tertan narrowed his eyes and glanced sidewise at Howe. His strange mouth smiled. Then in quizzical acceptance, he ducked his head, threw back the heavy dank lock, dropped into a seat with a great loose noise and began to write rapidly.

The room fell silent again and Howe resumed his idleness. When the bell rang, the students who had groaned when the task had been set now groaned again because they had not finished. Howe took up the papers and held the class while he made the first assignment. When he dismissed it, Tertan bore down on him, his slack mouth held ready for speech.

"Some professors," he said, "are pedants. They are Dryasdusts. However, some professors are free souls and creative spirits. Kant, Hegel, and Nietzsche were all professors." With this pronouncement he paused. "It is my opinion," he continued, "that you occupy the second category."

Howe looked at the boy in surprise and said with good-natured irony: "With Kant, Hegel and Nietzsche?"

Not only Tertan's hand and head but his whole awkward body waved away the stupidity. "It is the kind and not the quantity of the kind," he said sternly.

Rebuked, Howe said as simply and seriously as he could: "It would be nice to think so." He added: "Of course, I am not a professor."

This was clearly a disappointment but Tertan met it. "In the French sense," he said with composure. "Generically, a teacher."

Suddenly he bowed. It was such a bow, Howe fancied, as a stage-director might teach an actor playing a medieval student who takes leave of Abelard — stiff, solemn, with elbows close to the body and feet together. Then, quite as suddenly, he turned and left.

A queer fish, and as soon as Howe reached his office he sifted through the batch of themes and drew out Tertan's. The boy had filled many sheets with his unformed headlong scrawl. "Who am I?" he had begun. "Here, in a mundane, not to say commercialized academe, is asked the question which from time long immemorably out of mind has accreted doubts and thoughts in the psyche of man to pester him as a nuisance. Whether in St Augustine (or Austin as sometimes called) or Miss Bashkirtseff or Frederic Amiel or Empedocles, or in less lights of the intellect than these, this posed question has been ineluctable."

Howe took out his pencil. He circled "academe" and wrote "vocab" in the margin. He underlined "time long immemorably out of mind" and wrote "Diction!" But this seemed inadequate for what was wrong. He put down his pencil and read ahead to discover the principle of error in the theme.

"Today as ever, in spite of gloomy prophets of the dismal science (economics) the question is uninvalidated. Out of the starry depths of heaven hurtles this spear of query demanding to be caught on the shield of the mind ere it pierces the skull and the limbs be unstrung."

Baffled but quite caught, Howe read on. "Materialism, by which is meant the philosophic concept and not the moral idea, provides no aegis against the question which lies beyond the tangible (metaphysics). Existence without alloy is the question presented. Environment and heredity relegated aside, the rags and old clothes of practical life discarded, the name and the instrumentality of livelihood do not, as the prophets of the dismal science insist on in this connection, give solution to the interrogation which not from the professor merely but veritably from the cosmos is given. I think, therefore I am (cogito, etc.) but who am I? Tertan I am, but what is Tertan? Of this time, of that place, of some parentage, what does it matter?"

Existence without alloy: the phrase established itself. Howe put aside Tertan's paper and at random picked up another. "I am Arthur J. Casebeer, Jr," he read. "My father is Arthur J. Casebeer and my grandfather was Arthur J. Casebeer before him. My mother is Nina Wimble Casebeer. Both of them are college graduates and my father is in insurance. I was born in St Louis eighteen years ago and we still make our residence there."

Arthur J. Casebeer, who knew who he was, was less interesting than Tertan, but more coherent. Howe picked up Tertan's paper again. It was clear than none of the routine marginal comments, no "sent. str." or "punct." or "vocab." could cope with this torrential rhetoric. He read ahead, contenting himself with underscoring the errors against the time when he should have the necessary "conference" with Tertan.

It was a busy and official day of cards and sheets, arrangements and small decisions, and it gave Howe pleasure. Even when it was time to attend the first of the weekly Convocations he felt the charm of the beginning of things when intention is still innocent and uncorrupted by effort. He sat among the young instructors on the platform and joined in their humorous complaints at having to assist at the ceremony, but actually he got a clear satisfaction from the ritual of prayer and prosy speech and even from wearing his academic gown. And when the Convocation was over the pleasure continued as he crossed the campus, exchanging greetings with men he had not seen since the spring. They were people who did not yet, and perhaps never would, mean much to him, but in a year they had grown amiably to be part of his life. They were his fellow-townsmen.

The day had cooled again at sunset and there was a bright chill in the September twilight. Howe carried his voluminous gown over his arm, he swung his doctoral hood by its purple neckpiece and on his head he wore his mortarboard with its heavy gold tassel bobbing just over his eye. These were the weighty and absurd symbols of his new profession and they pleased him. At twenty-six Joseph Howe had discovered that he was neither so well off nor so Bohemian as he had once thought. A small income, adequate when supplemented by a sizeable cash legacy, was genteel poverty when the cash was all spent. And the literary life — the room at the Lafayette or the small apartment without a lease, the long summers on the Cape, the long afternoons and the social evenings — began to weary him. His writing filled his mornings and should perhaps have filled his life, yet it did not. To the amusement of his friends and with a certain sense that he was be-traying his own freedom, he had used the last of his legacy for a year at Harvard. The small but respectable reputation of his two volumes of verse had proved useful — he continued at Harvard on a fellowship and when he emerged as Dr Howe he received an excellent appoint-ment, with prospects, at Dwight.

He had his moments of fear when all that had ever been said of the dangers of the academic life had occurred to him. But after a year in which he had tested every possibility of corruption and seduction he was ready to rest easy. His third volume of verse, most of it written in his first year of teaching, was not only ampler but, he thought, better than its predecessors.

There was a clear hour before the Bradby dinner-party and Howe looked forward to it. But he was not to enjoy it, for lying with his mail on the hall table was a copy of this quarter's issue of *Life and Letters*, to which his landlord subscribed. Its severe cover announced that its editor, Frederic Woolley, had this month contributed an essay called "Two Poets", and Howe, picking it up, curious to see who the two poets might be, felt his own name start out at him with cabalistic power — Joseph Howe. As he continued to turn the pages his hand trembled.

Standing in the dark hall, holding the neat little magazine, Howe knew that his literary contempt for Frederic Woolley meant nothing, for he suddenly understood how he respected Woolley in the way of the world. He knew this by the trembling of his hand. And of the little world as well as the great, for although the literary groups of New York might dismiss Woolley, his name carried high authority in the academic world. At Dwight it was even a revered name, for it had been here at the college that Frederic Woolley had made the distinguished scholarly career from which he had gone on to literary journalism. In middle life he had been induced to take the editorship of *Life and Letters,* a literary monthly not widely read but heavily endowed and in its pages he had carried on the defence of what he sometimes called the older values. He was not without wit, he had great knowledge and considerable taste and even in the full movement of the "new" literature he had won a certain respect for his refusal to accept it. In France, even in England, he would have been connected with a more robust tradition of conservatism, but America gave him an audience not much better than genteel. It was known in the college that to the subsidy of *Life and Letters* the Bradbys contributed a great part.

As Howe read, he saw that he was involved in nothing less than an event. When the Fifth Series of *Studies in Order and Value* came to be collected, this latest of Frederic Woolley's essays would not be merely another step in the old direction. Clearly and unmistakably, it was a turning-point. All his literary life Woolley had been concerned with the relation of literature to morality, religion, and the private and delicate pieties, and he had been unalterably opposed to all that he had called "inhuman humanitarianism". But here, suddenly, dramatically late, he had made an about-face, turning to the public life and to the humanitarian politics he had so long despised. This was the kind of incident the histories of literature make much of. Frederic Woolley was opening for himself a new career and winning a kind of new youth. He contrasted the two poets, Thomas Wormser who was admirable, Joseph Howe who was almost dangerous. He spoke of the "precious subjectivism" of Howe's verse. "In times like ours," he wrote, "with millions facing penury and want, one feels that the qualities of the *tour d'ivoire* are well-nigh inhuman, nearly insulting. The *tour d'ivoire* becomes the *tour d'ivresse* and it is not self-intoxicated poets that our people need." The essay said more: "The problem is one of meaning. I am not ignorant that the creed of the esoteric poets declares that a poem does not and should not *mean* anything, that it *is* something. But poetry is what the poet makes it, and if he is a true poet he makes what his society needs. And what is needed now is the tradition in which Mr Wormser writes, the true tradition of poetry. The Howes do no harm, but they do no good when positive good is demanded of all responsible men. Or do the Howes indeed do no harm? Perhaps Plato would have said they do, that in some ways theirs is the Phrygian music that turns men's minds from the struggle. Certainly it is true that Thomas Wormser writes in the lucid Dorian mode which sends men into battle with evil."

It was easy to understand why Woolley had chosen to praise Thomas Wormser. The long, lilting lines of *Corn Under Willows* hymned, as Woolley put it, the struggle for wheat in the Iowa fields and expressed the real lives of real people. But why out of the dozen more notable examples he had chosen Howe's little volume as the example of "precious subjectivism" was hard to guess. In a way it was funny, this multiplication of himself into "the Howes". And yet this becoming the multiform political symbol by whose creation Frederic Woolley gave the sign of a sudden new life, this use of him as a sacrifice whose blood was necessary for the rites of rejuvenation, made him feel oddly unclean.

Nor could Howe get rid of a certain practical resentment. As a poet he had a special and respectable place in the college life. But it might be another thing to be marked as the poet of a wilful and selfish obscurity.

As he walked to the Bradbys Howe was a little tense and defensive. It seemed to him that all the world knew of the "attack" and agreed with it. And indeed the Bradbys had read the essay, but Professor Bradby, a kind and pretentious man, said, "I see my old friend knocked you about a bit, my boy," and his wife Eugenia looked at Howe with her childlike blue eyes and said: "I shall *scold* Frederic for the untrue things he wrote about you. You aren't the least obscure." They beamed at him. In their genial snobbery they seemed to feel that he had distinguished himself. He was the leader of Howeism. He enjoyed the dinner-party as much as he had thought he would.

And in the following days, as he was more preoccupied with his duties, the incident was forgotten. His classes had ceased to be mere groups. Student after student detached himself from the mass and required or claimed a place in Howe's awareness. Of them all it was Tertan who first and most violently signalled his separate existence. A week after classes had begun Howe saw his silhouette on the frosted glass of his office door. It was motionless for a long time, perhaps stopped by the problem of whether or not to knock before entering. Howe called, "Come in!" and Tertan entered with his shambling stride.

He stood beside the desk, silent and at attention. When Howe asked him to sit down, he responded with a gesture of head and hand as if to say that such amenities were beside the point. Nevertheless he did take the chair. He put his ragged crammed brief-case between his legs. His face, which Howe now observed fully for the first time, was confusing, for it was made up of florid curves, the nose arched in the bone and voluted in the nostril, the mouth loose and soft and rather moist. Yet the face was so thin and narrow as to seem the very type of asceticism. Lashes of unusual length veiled the eyes and, indeed, it seemed as if there were a veil over the whole countenance. Before the words actually came, the face screwed itself into an attitude of preparation for them.

"You can confer with me now?" Tertan said.

"Yes, I'd be glad to. There are several things in your two themes I want to talk to you about." Howe reached for the packet of themes on his desk and sought for Tertan's. But the boy was waving them away.

"These are done perforce," he said. "Under the pressure of your requirement. They are not significant, mere duties." Again his great hand flapped vaguely to dismiss his themes. He leaned forward and gazed at his teacher. "You are," he said, "a man of letters? You are a poet?" It was more declaration than question.

"I should like to think so," Howe said.

At first Tertan accepted the answer with a show of appreciation, as though the understatement made a secret between himself and Howe. Then he chose to misunderstand. With his shrewd and disconcerting control of expression, he presented to Howe a puzzled grimace. "What does that mean?" he said.

Howe retracted the irony. "Yes, I am a poet." It sounded strange to say.

"That," Tertan said, "is a wonder." He corrected himself with his ducking head. "I mean that is wonderful."

Suddenly he dived at the miserable brief-case between his legs, put it on his knees and began to fumble with the catch, all intent on the difficulty it presented. Howe noted that his suit was worn thin, his shirt almost unclean. He became aware, even, of a vague and musty odour of garments worn too long in unaired rooms. Tertan conquered the lock and began to concentrate upon a search into the interior. At last he held what he was after, a torn and crumpled copy of *Life and Letters.*

"I learned it from here," he said, holding it out.

Howe looked at him sharply, his hackles a little up. But the boy's face was not only perfectly innocent, it even shone with a conscious admiration. Apparently nothing of the import of the essay had touched him except the wonderful fact that his teacher was a "man of letters". Yet this seemed too stupid and Howe, to test it, said "The man who wrote that doesn't think it's wonderful."

Tertan made a moist hissing sound as he cleared his mouth of saliva. His head, oddly loose on his neck, wove a pattern of contempt in the air. "A critic," he said, "who admits *prima facie* that he does not understand." Then he said grandly: "It is the inevitable fate."

It was absurd, yet Howe was not only aware of the absurdity but of a tension suddenly and wonderfully relaxed. Now that the "attack" was on the table between himself and this strange boy and subject to the boy's funny and absolutely certain contempt, the hidden force of his feeling was revealed to him in the very moment that it vanished. All unsuspected, there had been a film over the world, a transparent but discolouring haze of danger. But he had no time to stop over the brightened aspect of things. Tertan was going on. "I also am a man of letters. Putative."

"You have written a good deal?" Howe meant to be no more than polite and he was surprised at the tenderness he heard in his words.

Solemnly the boy nodded, threw back the dank lock and sucked in a deep anticipatory breath. "First, a work of homiletics, which is a defence of the principles of religious optimism against the pessimism of Schopenhauer and the humanism of Nietzsche."

"Humanism? Why do you call it humanism?"

"It is my nomenclature of making a deity of man," Tertan replied negligently. "Then three fictional works, novels. And numerous essays in science, combating materialism. Is it your duty to read these if I bring them to you?"

Howe answered simply: "No, it isn't exactly my duty, but I shall be happy to read them."

Tertan stood up and remained silent. He rested his bag on the chair. With a certain compunction — for it did not seem entirely proper that, of two men of letters, one should have the right to blue-pencil the other, to grade him or to question the quality of his "sentence structure" — Howe reached for Tertan's papers. But before he could take them up, the boy suddenly made his bow-to-Abelard, the stiff inclination of the body with the hands seeming to emerge from the scholar's gown. Then he was gone.

But after his departure something was still left of him. The timbre of his curious sentences, the downright finality of so quaint a phrase as "It is the inevitable fate" still rang in the air. Howe gave the warmth of his feelings to the new visitor who stood at the door announcing himself with a genteel clearing of the throat.

"Dr Howe, I believe?" the student said. A large hand advanced into the room and grasped Howe's hand. "Blackburn, sir, Theodore Blackburn, vice-president of the Student Council. A great pleasure, sir."

Out of a pair of ruddy cheeks a pair of small eyes twinkled good-naturedly. The large face, the large body were not so much fat as beefy and suggested something "typical", monk, politician, or innkeeper.

Blackburn took the seat beside Howe's desk. "I may have seemed to introduce myself in my public capacity, sir," he said. "But it is really as an individual that I came to see you. That is to say, as one of your students to be."

He spoke with an "English" intonation and he went on: "I was once an English major, sir."

For a moment Howe was startled, for the roast-beef look of the boy and the manner of his speech gave a second's credibility to one sense of his statement. Then the collegiate meaning of the phrase asserted itself, but some perversity made Howe say what was not really in good taste even with so forward a student: "Indeed? What regiment?"

Blackburn stared and then gave a little pouf-pouf of laughter. He waved the misapprehension away. "*Very* good, sir. It certainly is an ambiguous term." He chuckled in appreciation of Howe's joke, then cleared his throat to put it aside. "I look forward to taking your course in the romantic poets, sir," he said earnestly. "To me the romantic poets are the very crown of English literature."

Howe made a dry sound, and the boy, catching some meaning in it, said: "Little as I know them, of course. But even Shakespeare who is so dear to us of the Anglo-Saxon tradition is in a sense but the preparation for Shelley, Keats and Byron. And Wadsworth."

Almost sorry for him, Howe dropped his eyes. With some embarrassment, for the boy was not actually his student, he said softly: "Wordsworth."

"Sir?"

"Wordsworth, not Wadsworth. You said Wadsworth."

"Did I, sir?" Gravely he shook his head to rebuke himself for the error. "Wordsworth, of course — slip of the tongue." Then, quite in command again, he went on. "I have a favour to ask of you, Dr Howe. You see, I began my college course as an English major" — he smiled — "as I said."

"Yes?"

"But after my first year I shifted. I shifted to the social sciences. Sociology and government — I find them stimulating and very *real*." He paused, out of respect for reality. "But now I find that perhaps I have neglected the other side."

"The other side?" Howe said.

"Imagination, fancy, culture. A well-rounded man." He trailed off as if there were perfect understanding between them. "And so, sir, I have decided to end my senior year with your course in the romantic poets."

His voice was filled with an indulgence which Howe ignored as he said flatly and gravely: "But that course isn't given until the spring term."

"Yes, sir, and that is where the favour comes in. Would you let me take your romantic prose course? I can't take it for credit, sir, my programme is full, but just for background it seems to me that I ought to take it. I do hope," he concluded in a manly way, "that you will consent."

"Well, it's no great favour, Mr Blackburn. You can come if you wish, though there's not much point in it if you don't do the reading."

The bell rang for the hour and Howe got up.

"May I begin with this class, sir?" Blackburn's smile was candid and boyish.

Howe nodded carelessly and together, silently, they walked to the classroom down the hall. When they reached the door Howe stood back to let his student enter, but Blackburn moved adroitly behind him and grasped him by the arm to urge him over the threshold. They entered together with Blackburn's hand firmly on Howe's biceps, the student inducting the teacher into his own room. Howe felt a surge of temper rise in him and almost violently he disengaged his arm and walked to the desk, while Blackburn found a seat in the front row and smiled at him.

2

The question was: At whose door must the tragedy be laid?

All night the snow had fallen heavily and only now was abating in sparse little flurries. The windows were valanced high with white. It was very quiet, something of the quiet of the world had reached the class and Howe found that everyone was glad to talk or listen. In the room there was a comfortable sense of pleasure in being human.

Casebeer believed that the blame for the tragedy rested with heredity. Picking up the book he read: "The sins of the fathers are visited on their children." This opinion was received with general favour. Nevertheless Johnson ventured to say that the fault was all Pastor Manders' because the Pastor had made Mrs Alving go back to her husband and was always hiding the truth. To this Hibbard objected with logic enough: "Well, then, it was really all her husband's fault. He *did* all the bad things." De Witt, his face bright with an impatient idea, said that the fault was all society's. "By society I don't mean upper-crust society," he said. He looked around a little defiantly, taking in any members of the class who might be members of upper-crust society. "Not in that sense. I mean the social unit."

Howe nodded and said: "Yes, of course."

"If the society of the time had progressed far enough in science," De Witt went on, "then there would be no problem for Mr Ibsen to write about. Captain Alving plays around a little, gives way to perfectly natural biological urges, and he gets a social disease, venereal disease. If the disease is cured, no problem. Invent salvarsan and the disease is cured. The problem of heredity disappears and li'l Oswald just doesn't get paresis. No paresis, no problem — no problem, no play."

This was carrying the ark into battle and the class looked at De Witt with respectful curiosity. It was his usual way and on the whole they were sympathetic with his struggle to prove to Howe that science was better than literature. Still, there was something in his reckless manner that alienated them a little.

"Or take birth-control, for instance," De Witt went on. "If Mrs Alving had had some knowledge of contraception, she wouldn't have had to have li'l Oswald at all. No li'l Oswald, no play."

The class was suddenly quieter. In the back row Stettenhover swung his great football shoulders in a righteous sulking gesture, first to the right, then to the left. He puckered his mouth ostentatiously. Intellect was always ending up by talking dirty.

Tertan's hand went up and Howe said: "Mr Tertan." The boy shambled to his feet and began his long characteristic gulp. Howe made a motion with his fingers, as small as possible, and Tertan ducked his head and smiled in apology. He sat down. The class laughed. With more than half the term gone, Tertan had not been able to remember that one did not rise to speak. He seemed unable to carry on the life of the intellect without his mark of respect for it. To Howe the boy's habit of rising seemed to accord with the formal shabbiness of his dress. He never wore the casual sweaters and jackets of his classmates. Into the free and comfortable air of the college classroom he brought the stuffy sordid strictness of some crowded metropolitan high school.

"Speaking from one sense," Tertan began slowly, "there is no blame ascribable. From the sense of determinism, who can say where the blame lies? The pre-ordained is the preordained and it cannot be said without rebellion against the universe, a palpable absurdity."

In the back row Stettenhover slumped suddenly in his seat, his heels held out before him, making a loud dry disgusted sound. His body sank until his neck rested on the back of his chair. He folded his hands across his belly and looked significantly out of the window, exasperated not only with Tertan but with Howe, with the class, with the whole system designed to encourage this kind of thing. There was a certain insolence in the movement and Howe flushed. As Tertan continued to speak, Howe walked casually towards the window and placed himself in the line of Stettenhover's vision. He stared at the great fellow, who pretended not to see him. There was so much power in the big body, so much contempt in the Greek-athlete face under the crisp Greek-athlete curls, that Howe felt almost physical fear. But at last Stettenhover admitted him to focus and under his disapproving gaze sat up with slow indifference. His eyebrows raised high in resignation, he began to examine his hands. Howe relaxed and turned his attention back to Tertan.

"Flux of existence," Tertan was saying, "produces all things, so that judgment wavers. Beyond the phenomena, what? But phenomena are adumbrated and to them we are limited."

Howe saw it for a moment as perhaps it existed in the boy's mind — the world of shadows which are cast by a great light upon a hidden reality as in the old myth of the Cave. But the little brush with Stettenhover had tired him and he said irritably: "But come to the point, Mr Tertan."

He said it so sharply that some of the class looked at him curiously. For three months he had gently carried Tertan through his verbosities, to the vaguely respectful surprise of the other students, who seemed to conceive that there existed between this strange classmate and their teacher some special understanding from which they were content to be excluded. Tertan looked at him mildly and at once came brilliantly to the point. "This is the summation of the play," he said and took up his book and read: " 'Your poor father never found any outlet for the overmastering joy of life that was in him. And I brought no holiday into his home, either. Everything seemed to turn upon duty and I am afraid I made your poor father's home unbearable to him, Oswald.' Spoken by Mrs Alving."

Yes, that was surely the "summation" of the play and Tertan had hit it, as he hit, deviously and eventually, the literary point of almost everything. But now, as always, he was wrapping it away from sight. "For most mortals," he said, "there are only joys of biological urgings, gross and crass, such as the sensuous Captain Alving. For certain few there are the transmutations beyond these to a contemplation of the utter whole."

Oh, the boy was mad. And suddenly the word, used in hyperbole, intended almost for the expression of exasperate admiration, became literal. Now that the word was used, it became simply apparent to Howe that Tertan was mad.

It was a monstrous word and stood like a bestial thing in the room. Yet it so completely comprehended everything that had puzzled Howe, it so arranged and explained what for three months had been perplexing him that almost at once its horror became domesticated. With this word Howe was able to understand why he had never been able to communicate to Tertan the value of a single criticism or correction of his wild, verbose themes. Their conferences had been frequent and long but had done nothing to reduce to order the splendid confusion of the boy's ideas. Yet, impossible though its expression was, Tertan's incandescent mind could always strike for a moment into some dark corner of thought.

And now it was suddenly apparent that it was not a faulty rhetoric that Howe had to contend with. With his new knowledge he looked at Tertan's face and wondered how he could have so long deceived himself. Tertan was still talking and the class had lapsed into a kind of patient unconsciousness, a coma of respect for words which, for all that most of them knew, might be profound. Almost with a suffusion of shame, Howe believed that in some dim way the class had long ago had some intimation of Tertan's madness. He reached out as decisively as he could to seize the thread of Tertan's discourse before it should be entangled further.

"Mr Tertan says that the blame must be put upon whoever kills the joy of living in another. We have been assuming that Captain Alving was a wholly bad man, but what if we assume that he became bad only because Mrs Alving, when they were first married, acted towards him in the prudish way she says she did?"

It was a ticklish idea to advance to freshmen and perhaps not profitable. Not all of them were following.

"That would put the blame on Mrs Alving herself, whom most of you admire. And she herself seems to think so." He glanced at his watch. The hour was nearly over. "What do you think, Mr De Witt?"

De Witt rose to the idea, wanted to know if society couldn't be blamed for educating Mrs Alving's temperament in the wrong way. Casebeer was puzzled, Stettenhover continued to look at his hands until the bell rang.

Tertan, his brows louring in thought, was making as always for a private word. Howe gathered his books and papers to leave quickly. At this moment of his discovery and with the knowledge still raw, he could not engage himself with Tertan. Tertan sucked in his breath to prepare for speech and Howe made ready for the pain and confusion. But at that moment Casebeer detached himself from the group with which he had been conferring and which he seemed to represent. His constituency remained at a tactful distance. The mission involved the time of an assigned essay. Casebeer's presentation of the plea — it was based on the freshmen's heavy duties at the fraternities during Carnival Week — cut across Tertan's preparations for speech. "And so some of us fellows thought," Casebeer concluded with heavy solemnity, "that we could do a better job, give our minds to it more, if we had more time."

Tertan regarded Casebeer with mingled curiosity and revulsion. Howe not only said that he would postpone the assignment but went on to talk about the Carnival and even drew the waiting constituency into the conversation. He was conscious of Tertan's stern and astonished stare, then of his sudden departure.

Now that the fact was clear, Howe knew that he must act on it. His course was simple enough. He must lay the case before the Dean. Yet he hesitated. His feeling for Tertan must now, certainly, be in some way invalidated. Yet could he, because of a word, hurry to assign to official and reasonable solicitude what had been, until this moment, so various and warm? He could at least delay and, by moving slowly, lend a poor grace to the necessary, ugly act of making his report.

It was with some notion of keeping the matter in his own hands that he went to the Dean's office to look up Tertan's records. In the outer office the Dean's secretary greeted him brightly and at his request brought him the manila folder with the small identifying photograph pasted in the corner. She laughed. "He was looking for the birdie in the wrong place," she said.

Howe leaned over his shoulder to look at the picture. It was as bad as all the Dean's office photographs were, but it differed from all that Howe had ever seen. Tertan, instead of looking into the camera, as no doubt he had been bidden, had, at the moment of exposure, turned his eyes upward. His mouth, as though conscious of the trick played on the photographer, had the sly superior look that Howe knew.

The secretary was fascinated by the picture. "What a funny boy," she said. "He looks like Tartuffe!"

And so he did, with the absurd piety of the eyes and the conscious slyness of the mouth and the whole face bloated by the bad lens.

"Is he *like* that?" the secretary said.

"Like Tartuffe? No."

From the photograph there was little enough comfort to be had. The records themselves gave no clue to madness, though they suggested sadness enough. Howe read of a father, Stanislaus Tertan, born in Budapest and trained in engineering in Berlin, once employed by the Hercules Chemical Corporation — this was one of the factories that dominated the south end of the town — but now without employment. He read of a mother Erminie (Youngfellow) Tertan, born in Manchester, educated at a Normal School at Leeds, now housewife by profession. The family lived on Greenbriar Street, which Howe knew as a row of once elegant homes near what was now the factory district. The old mansions had long ago been divided into small and primitive apartments. Of Ferdinand himself there was little to learn. He lived with his parents, had attended a Detroit high school and had transferred to the local school in his last year. His rating for intelligence as expressed in numbers, was high, his scholastic record was remarkable, he held a college scholarship for his tuition.

Howe laid the folder on the secretary's desk. "Did you find what you wanted to know?" she asked.

The phrases from Tertan's momentous first theme came back to him. "Tertan I am, but what is Tertan? Of this time, of that place, of some parentage, what does it matter?"

"No, I didn't find it," he said.

Now that he had consulted the sad half-meaningless record he knew all the more firmly that he must not give the matter out of his own hands. He must not release Tertan to authority. Not that he anticipated from the Dean anything but the greatest kindness for Tertan. The Dean would have the experience and skill which he himself could not have. One way or another the Dean could answer the question: "What is Tertan?" Yet this was precisely what he feared. He alone could keep alive — not for ever but for a somehow important time — the question: "What is Tertan?" He alone could keep it still a question. Some sure instinct told him that he must not surrender the question to a clean official desk in a clear official light to be dealt with, settled and closed.

He heard himself saying: "Is the Dean busy at the moment? I'd like to see him."

His request came thus unbidden, even forbidden, and it was one of the surprising and startling incidents of his life. Later, when he reviewed the events, so disconnected in themselves or so merely odd, of the story that unfolded for him that year, it was over this moment, on its face the least notable, that he paused longest. It was frequently to be with fear and never without a certainty of its meaning in his own knowledge of himself that he would recall this simple, routine request and the feeling of shame and freedom it gave him as he sent everything down the official chute. In the end, of course, no matter what he did to "protect" Tertan, he would have had to make the same request and lay the matter on the Dean's clean desk. But it would always be a landmark of his life that, at the very moment when he was rejecting the official way, he had been, without will or intention, so gladly drawn to it.

After the storm's last delicate flurry, the sun had come out. Reflected by the new snow, it filled the office with a golden light which was almost musical in the way it made all the commonplace objects of efficiency shine with a sudden sad and noble significance. And the light, now that he noticed it, made the utterance of his perverse and unwanted request even more momentous.

The secretary consulted the engagement pad. "He'll be free any minute. Don't you want to wait in the parlour?"

She threw open the door of the large and pleasant room in which the Dean held his Committee meetings and in which his visitors waited. It was designed with a homely elegance on the masculine side of the eighteenth-century manner. There was a small coal fire in the grate and the handsome mahogany table was strewn with books and magazines. The large windows gave on the snowy lawn and there was such a fine width of window that the white casements and walls seemed at this moment but a continuation of the snow, the snow but an extension of casement and walls. The outdoors seemed taken in and made safe, the indoors seemed luxuriously freshened and expanded.

Howe sat down by the fire and lighted a cigarette. The room had its intended effect upon him. He felt comfortable and relaxed, yet nicely organized, some young diplomatic agent of the eighteenth century, the newly fledged Swift carrying out Sir William Temple's business. The rawness of Tertan's case quite vanished. He crossed his legs and reached for a magazine.

It was that famous issue of *Life and Letters* that his idle hand had found and his blood raced as he sifted through it and the shape of his own name, Joseph Howe, sprang out at him, still cabalistic in its power. He tossed the magazine back on the table as the door of the Dean's office opened and the Dean ushered out Theodore Blackburn.

"Ah, Joseph!" the Dean said.

Blackburn said: "Good morning, Doctor." Howe winced at the title and caught the flicker of amusement over the Dean's face. The Dean stood with his hand high on the door-jamb and Blackburn, still in the doorway, remained standing almost under his long arm.

Howe nodded briefly to Blackburn, snubbing his eager deference. "Can you give me a few minutes?" he said to the Dean.

"All the time you want. Come in." Before the two men could enter the office, Blackburn claimed their attention with a long full "Er". As they turned to him, Blackburn said: "Can *you* give *me* a few minutes,

Dr Howe?" His eyes sparkled at the little audacity he had committed, the slightly impudent play with hierarchy. Of the three of them Blackburn kept himself the lowest, but he reminded Howe of his subaltern relation to the Dean.

"I mean, of course," Blackburn went on easily, "when you've finished with the Dean."

"I'll be in my office shortly," Howe said, turned his back on the ready "Thank you, sir", and followed the Dean into the inner room.

"Energetic boy", said the Dean. "A bit beyond himself but very energetic. Sit down."

The Dean lighted a cigarette, leaned back in his chair, sat easy and silent for a moment, giving Howe no signal to go ahead with business. He was a young Dean, not much beyond forty, a tall handsome man with sad, ambitious eyes. He had been a Rhodes scholar. His friends looked for great things from him and it was generally said that he had notions of education which he was not yet ready to try to put into practice.

His relaxed silence was meant as a compliment to Howe. He smiled and said: "What's the business, Joseph?"

"Do you know Tertan — Ferdinand Tertan, a freshman?"

The Dean's cigarette was in his mouth and his hands were clasped behind his head. He did not seem to search his memory for the name. He said: "What about him?"

Clearly the Dean knew something and he was waiting for Howe to tell him more. Howe moved only tentatively. Now that he was doing what he had resolved not to do, he felt more guilty at having been so long deceived by Tertan and more need to be loyal to his error.

"He's a strange fellow," he ventured. He said stubbornly: "In a strange way he's very brilliant." He concluded: "But very strange."

The springs of the Dean's swivel chair creaked as he came out of his sprawl and leaned forward to Howe. "Do you mean he's so strange that it's something you could give a name to?"

Howe looked at him stupidly. "What do you mean?" he said.

"What's his trouble?" the Dean said more neutrally.

"He's very brilliant, in a way. I looked him up and he has a top intelligence rating. But somehow, and it's hard to explain just how, what he says is always on the edge of sense and doesn't quite make it."

The Dean looked at him and Howe flushed up. The Dean had surely read Woolley on the subject of "the Howes" and the *tour d'ivresse*. Was that quick glance ironical?

The Dean picked up some papers from his desk and Howe could see that they were in Tertan's impatient scrawl. Perhaps the little gleam in the Dean's glance had come only from putting facts together. "He sent me this yesterday," the Dean said. "After an interview I had with him. I haven't been able to do more than glance at it. When you said what you did, I realized there was something wrong."

Twisting his mouth, the Dean looked over the letter. "You seem to be involved," he said, without looking up. "By the way, what did you give him at mid-term?"

Flushing, setting his shoulders, Howe said firmly: "I gave him A-minus."

The Dean chuckled. "Might be a good idea if some of our nicer boys went crazy — just a little." He said, "Well," to conclude the matter and handed the papers to Howe. "See if this is the same thing you've been finding. Then we can go into the matter again."

Before the fire in the parlour, in the chair that Howe had been occupying, sat Blackburn. He sprang to his feet as Howe entered.

"I said my office, Mr Blackburn." Howe's voice was sharp. Then he was almost sorry for the rebuke, so clearly and naively did Blackburn seem to relish his stay in the parlour, close to authority.

"I'm in a bit of a hurry, sir," he said, "and I did want to be sure to speak to you, sir."

He was really absurd, yet fifteen years from now he would have grown up to himself, to the assurance and mature beefiness. In banks, in consular offices, in brokerage firms, on the bench, more seriously affable, a little sterner, he would make use of his ability to be administered by his job. It was almost reassuring. Now he was exercising his too-great skill on Howe. "I owe you an apology, sir," he said.

Howe knew that he did but he showed surprise.

"I mean, Doctor, after your having been so kind about letting me attend your class, I stopped coming." He smiled in deprecation. "Extra-curricular activities take up so much of my time, I'm afraid I undertook more than I could perform."

Howe had noticed the absence and had been a little irritated by it after Blackburn's elaborate plea. It was an absence that might be interpreted as a comment on the teacher. But there was only one way for him to answer. "You've no need to apologize," he said, "It's wholly your affair."

Blackburn beamed. "I'm so glad you feel that way about it, sir. I was worried you might think I had stayed away because I was influenced by — " He stopped and lowered his eyes.

Astonished, Howe said: "Influenced by what?"

"Well, by — " Blackburn hesitated and for answer pointed to the tablet on which lay the copy of *Life and Letters*. Without looking at it, he knew where to direct his hand. "By the unfavourable publicity, sir." He hurried on. "And that brings me to another point, sir. I am secretary of Quill and Scroll, sir, the student literary society, and I wonder if you would address us. You could read your own poetry, sir, and defend your own point of view. It would be very interesting."

It was truly amazing. Howe looked long and cruelly into Blackburn's face, trying to catch the secret of the mind that could have conceived this way of manipulating him, this way so daring and inept — but not entirely inept — with its malice so without malignity. The face did not yield its secret. Howe smiled broadly and said: "Of course I don't think you were influenced by the unfavourable publicity."

"I'm still going to take — regularly, for credit — your romantic poets course next term," Blackburn said.

"Don't worry, my dear fellow, don't worry about it."

Howe started to leave and Blackburn stopped him with: "But about Quill, sir?"

"Suppose we wait until next term? I'll be less busy then.'"

And Blackburn said: "Very good, sir, and thank you."

In his office the little encounter seemed less funny to Howe, was even in some indeterminate way disturbing. He made an effort to put it from his mind by turning to what was sure to disturb him more, the Tertan letter read in the new interpretation. He found what he had always found, the same florid leaps beyond fact and meaning, the same headlong certainty. But as his eye passed over the familiar scrawl it caught his own name and for the second time that hour he felt the race of his blood.

"The Paraclete," Tertan had written to the Dean, "from a Greek word meaning to stand in place of, but going beyond the primitive idea to mean traditionally the helper, the one who comforts and assists, cannot without fundamental loss be jettisoned. Even if taken no longer in the supernatural sense, the concept remains in the human consciousness inevitably. Humanitarianism is no reply, for not every man stands in the place of every other man for this other's comrade comfort. But certain are chosen out of the human race to be the consoler of some other. Of these, for example, is Joseph Barker Howe, Ph.D. Of intellects not the first yet of true intellect and lambent instructions, given to that which is intuitive and irrational, not to what is logical in the strict word, what is judged by him is of the heart and not the head. Here is one chosen, in that he chooses himself to stand in the place of another for comfort and consolation. To him more than any other I give my gratitude, with all respect to our Dean who reads this, a noble man, but merely dedicated, not consecrated. But not in the aspect of the Paraclete only is Dr Joseph Barker Howe established, for he must be the Paraclete to another aspect of himself, that which is driven and persecuted by the lack of understanding in the world at large, so that he in himself embodies the full history of man's tribulations and, overflowing upon others, notably the present writer, is the ultimate end."

This was love. There was no escape from it. Try as Howe might to remember that Tertan was mad and all his emotions invalidated, he could not destroy the effect upon him of his student's stern, affectionate regard. He had betrayed not only a power of mind but a power of love. And however firmly he held before his attention the fact of Tertan's madness, he could do nothing to banish the physical sensation of gratitude he felt. He had never thought of himself as "driven and persecuted" and he did not now. But still he could not make meaningless his sensation of gratitude. The pitiable Tertan sternly pitied him, and comfort came from Tertan's never-to-be-comforted mind.

3

In an academic community, even an efficient one, official matters move slowly. The term drew to a close with no action in the case of

Tertan, and Joseph Howe had to confront a curious problem. How should he grade his strange student, Tertan?

Tertan's final examination had been no different from all his other writing, and what did one "give" such a student? De Witt must have his A, that was clear. Johnson would get a B. With Casebeer it was a question of a B-minus or a C-plus, and Stettenhover, who had been crammed by the team tutor to fill half a blue-book with his thin feminine scrawl, would have his C-minus which he would accept with mingled indifference and resentment. But with Tertan it was not so easy.

The boy was still in the college process and his name could not be omitted from the grade sheet. Yet what should a mind under suspicion of madness be graded? Until the medical verdict was given, it was for Howe to continue as Tertan's teacher and to keep his judgment pedagogical. Impossible to give him an F: he had not failed. B was for Johnson's stolid mediocrity. He could not be put on the edge of passing with Stettenhover, for he exactly did not pass. In energy and richness of intellect he was perhaps even De Witt's superior, and Howe toyed grimly with the notion of giving him an A, but that would lower the value of the A De Witt had won with his beautiful and clear, if still arrogant, mind. There was a notation which the Registrar recognized — Inc for Incomplete and in the horrible comedy of the situation, Howe considered that. But really only a mark of M for Mad would serve.

In his perplexity, Howe sought the Dean, but the Dean was out of town. In the end, he decided to maintain the A-minus he had given Tertan at mid-term. After all, there had been no falling away from that quality. He entered it on the grade sheet with something like bravado.

Academic time moves quickly. A college year is not really a year, lacking as it does three months. And it is endlessly divided into units, which at their beginning, appear larger than they are — terms, half-terms, months, weeks. And the ultimate unit, the hour, is not really an hour, lacking as it does ten minutes. And so the new term advanced rapidly and one day the fields about the town were all brown, cleared of even the few thin patches of snow which had lingered so long.

Howe, as he lectured on the romantic poets, became conscious of

Blackburn emanating wrath. Blackburn did it well, did it with enormous dignity. He did not stir in his seat, he kept his eyes fixed on Howe in perfect attention, but he abstained from using his note-book, there was no mistaking what he proposed to himself as an attitude. His elbow on the writing-wing of the chair, his chin on the curled fingers of his hand, he was the embodiment of intellectual indignation. He was thinking his own thoughts, would give no public offence, yet would claim his due, was not to be intimidated. Howe knew that he would present himself at the end of the hour.

Blackburn entered the office without invitation. He did not smile, there was no cajolery about him. Without invitation he sat down beside Howe's desk. He did not speak until he had taken the blue-book from his pocket. He said: "What does this mean, sir?"

It was a sound and conservative student tactic. Said in the usual way it meant: "How could you have so misunderstood me?" or "What does this mean for my future in the course?" But there were none of the humbler tones in Blackburn's way of saying it.

Howe made the established reply: "I think that's for you to tell me."

Blackburn continued icy. "I'm sure I can't, sir."

There was a silence between them. Both dropped their eyes to the blue-book on the desk. On its cover Howe had pencilled: "F. This is very poor work."

Howe picked up the blue-book. There was always the possibility of injustice. The teacher may be bored by the mass of papers and not wholly attentive. A phrase, even the student's handwriting, may irritate him unreasonably. "Well," said Howe, "let's go through it."

He opened the first page. "Now here: you write: 'In the *Ancient Mariner*, Coleridge lives in and transports us to a honey-sweet world where all is rich and strange, a world of charm to which we can escape from the humdrum existence of our daily lives, the world of romance. Here, in this warm and honey-sweet land of charming dreams we can relax and enjoy ourselves.'"

Howe lowered the papers and waited with a neutral look for Blackburn to speak. Blackburn returned the look boldly, did not speak, sat stolid and lofty. At last Howe said, speaking gently: "Did you mean that, or were you just at a loss for something to say?"

"You imply that I was just 'bluffing'?" The quotation marks hung palpable in the air about the word.

"I'd like to know. I'd prefer believing that you were bluffing to believing that you really thought this."

Blackburn's eyebrows went up. From the height of a great and firm-based idea he looked at his teacher. He clasped the crags for a moment and then pounced, craftily, suavely. "Do you mean, Dr Howe, that there aren't two opinions possible?"

It was superbly done in its air of putting all of Howe's intellectual life into the balance. Howe remained patient and simple. "Yes, many opinions are possible, but not this one. Whatever anyone believes of the *Ancient Mariner,* no one can in reason believe that it represents a — a honey-sweet world in which we can relax."

"But that is what I *feel*, sir."

This was well done, too. Howe said: "Look, Mr Blackburn. Do you really relax with hunger and thirst, the heat and the sea-serpents, the dead men with staring eyes, Life in Death and the skeletons? Come now, Mr Blackburn."

Blackburn made no answer and Howe pressed forward. "Now you say of Wordsworth: 'Of peasant stock himself, he turned from the effete life of the salons and found in the peasant the hope of a flaming revolution which would sweep away all the old ideas. This is the subject of his best poems.' "

Beaming at his teacher with youthful eagerness, Blackburn said: "Yes, sir, a rebel, a bringer of light to suffering mankind. I see him as a kind of Prothemeus."

"A kind of what?"

"Prothemeus, sir."

"Think, Mr Blackburn. We were talking about him only today and I mentioned his name a dozen times. You don't mean Prothemeus. You mean — " Howe waited but there was no response.

"You mean Prometheus."

Blackburn gave no assent and Howe took the reins. "You've done a bad job here, Mr Blackburn, about as bad as could be done." He saw Blackburn stiffen and his genial face harden again. "It shows either a lack of preparation or a complete lack of understanding." He saw Blackburn's face begin to go to pieces and he stopped.

"Oh, sir," Blackburn burst out. "I've never had a mark like this before, never anything below a B, never. A thing like this has never happened to me before."

It must be true, it was a statement too easily verified. Could it be that other instructors accepted such flaunting nonsense? Howe wanted to end the interview. "I'll set it down to lack of preparation," he said. "I know you're busy. That's not an excuse but it's an explanation. Now suppose you really prepare and then take another quiz in two weeks. We'll forget this one and count the other."

Blackburn squirmed with pleasure and gratitude. "Thank you, sir. You're really very kind, very kind."

Howe rose to conclude the visit. "All right then — in two weeks."

It was that day that the Dean imparted to Howe the conclusion of the case of Tertan. It was simple and a little anti-climactic. A physician had been called in, and had said the word, given the name.

"A classic case, he called it," the Dean said. "Not a doubt in the world," he said. His eyes were full of miserable pity and he clutched at a word. "A classic case, a classic case." To his aid and to Howe's there came the Parthenon and the form of the Greek drama, the Aristotelian logic, Racine and the Well-Tempered Clavichord, the blueness of the Aegean and its clear sky. Classic — that is to say, without a doubt, perfect in its way, a veritable model, and, as the Dean had been told, sure to take a perfectly predictable and inevitable course to a foreknown conclusion.

It was not only pity that stood in the Dean's eyes. For a moment there was fear too. "Terrible," he said, "it is simply terrible."

Then he went on briskly. "Naturally we've told the boy nothing. And naturally we won't. His tuition's paid by his scholarship and we'll continue him on the rolls until the end of the year. That will be kindest. After that the matter will be out of our control. We'll see, of course, that he gets into the proper hands. I'm told there will be no change, he'll go on like this, be as good as this, for four to six months. And so we'll just go along as usual."

So Tertan continued to sit in Section 5 of English 1A, to his classmates still a figure of curiously dignified fun, symbol to most of them of the respectable but absurd intellectual life. But to his teacher he was now very different. He had not changed — he was still the greyhound casting for the scent of ideas and Howe could see that he was still the same Tertan, but he could not feel it. What he felt as he looked at the boy sitting in his accustomed place was the hard blank of a fact. The fact itself was formidable and depressing. But what Howe was chiefly aware of was that he had permitted the metamorphosis of Tertan from person to fact.

As much as possible he avoided seeing Tertan's upraised hand and eager eye. But the fact did not know of its mere factuality, it continued its existence as if it were Tertan, hand up and eye questioning, and one day it appeared in Howe's office with a document.

"Even the spirit who lives egregiously, above the herd, must have its relations with the fellow-man," Tertan declared. He laid the document on Howe's desk. It was headed "Quill and Scroll Society of Dwight College. Application for Membership".

"In most ways these are crass minds," Tertan said, touching the paper. "Yet as a whole, bound together in their common love of letters, they transcend their intellectual lacks, since it is not a paradox that the whole is greater than the sum of its parts."

"When are the elections?" Howe asked.

"They take place tomorrow."

"I certainly hope you will be successful."

"Thank you. Would you wish to implement that hope?" A rather dirty finger pointed to the bottom of the sheet. "A faculty recommender is necessary," Tertan said stiffly, and waited.

"And you wish me to recommend you?"

"It would be an honour."

"You may use my name."

Tertan's finger pointed again. "It must be a written sponsorship, signed by the sponsor." There was a large blank space on the form under the heading: "Opinion of Faculty Sponsor."

This was almost another thing and Howe hesitated. Yet there was nothing else to do and he took out his fountain-pen. He wrote: "Mr Ferdinand Tertan is marked by his intense devotion to letters and by his exceptional love of all things of the mind." To this he signed his name which looked bold and assertive on the white page. It disturbed him, the strange affirming power of a name. With a business-like air, Tertan whipped up the paper, folded it with decision and put it into his pocket. He bowed and took his departure, leaving Howe with the sense of having done something oddly momentous.

And so much now seemed odd and momentous to Howe that should not have seemed so. It was odd and momentous, he felt, when he sat with Blackburn's second quiz before him and wrote in an excessively firm hand the grade of C-minus. The paper was a clear, an indisputable failure. He was carefully and consciously committing a cowardice. Blackburn had told the truth when he had pleaded his past record. Howe had consulted it in the Dean's office. It showed no grade lower than a B-minus. A canvass of some of Blackburn's previous instructors had brought vague attestations to the adequate powers of a student imperfectly remembered and sometimes surprise that his abilities could be questioned at all.

As he wrote the grade, Howe told himself that this cowardice sprang from an unwillingness to have more dealings with a student he disliked. He knew it was simpler than that. He knew he feared Blackburn: that was the absurd truth. And cowardice did not solve the matter after all. Blackburn, flushed with a first success, attacked at once. The minimal passing grade had not assuaged his feelings, and he sat at Howe's desk and again the blue-book lay between them. Blackburn said nothing. With an enormous impudence, he was waiting for Howe to speak and explain himself.

At last Howe said sharply and rudely: "Well?" His throat was tense and the blood was hammering in his head. His mouth was tight with anger at himself for his disturbance.

Blackburn's glance was almost baleful. "This is impossible, sir."

"But there it is," Howe answered.

"Sir?" Blackburn had not caught the meaning but his tone was still haughty.

Impatiently Howe said: "There it is, plain as day. Are you here to complain again?"

"Indeed I am, sir." There was surprise in Blackburn's voice that Howe should ask the question.

"I shouldn't complain if I were you. You did a throughly bad job on your first quiz. This one is a little, only a very little better." This was not true. If anything, it was worse.

"That might be a matter of opinion, sir."

"It is a matter of opinion. Of my opinion."

"Another opinion might be different, sir."

"You really believe that?" Howe said.

"Yes." The omission of the 'sir' was monumental.

"Whose, for example?"

"The Dean's, for example." Then the fleshy jaw came forward a little. "Or a certain literary critic's, for example."

It was colossal and almost too much for Blackburn himself to handle. The solidity of his face almost crumpled under it. But he withstood his own audacity and went on. "And the Dean's opinion might be guided by the knowledge that the person who gave me this mark is the man whom a famous critic, the most eminent judge of literature in this country, called a drunken man. The Dean might think twice about whether such a man is fit to teach Dwight students."

Howe said in quiet admonition, "Blackburn, you're mad", meaning no more than to check the boy's extravagance.

But Blackburn paid no heed. He had another shot in the locker. "And the Dean might be guided by the information, of which I have evidence, documentary evidence" — he slapped his breast-pocket twice — "that this same person personally recommended to the college literary society, the oldest in the country, that he personally recommended a student who is crazy, who threw the meeting into an uproar, a psychiatric case. The Dean might take that into account."

Howe was never to learn the details of that 'uproar'. He had always to content himself with the dim but passionate picture which at that moment sprang into his mind, of Tertan standing on some abstract height and madly denouncing the multitude of Quill and Scroll who howled him down.

He sat quiet a moment and looked at Blackburn. The ferocity had entirely gone from the student's face. He sat regarding his teacher almost benevolently. He had played a good card and now, scarcely at all unfriendly, he was waiting to see the effect. Howe took up the blue-book and negligently sifted through it. He read a page, closed the book, struck out the C-minus and wrote an F.

"Now you may take the paper to the Dean," he said. "You may tell him that after reconsidering it, I lowered the grade."

The gasp was audible. "Oh, sir!" Blackburn cried. "Please!" His face was agonized. "It means my graduation, my livelihood, my future. Don't do this to me."

"It's done already."

Blackburn stood up. "I spoke rashly, sir, hastily. I had no intention, no real intention, of seeing the Dean. It rests with you — entirely, entirely. I *hope* you will restore the first mark."

"Take the matter to the Dean or not, just as you choose. The grade is what you deserve and it stands."

Blackburn's head dropped. "And will I be failed at mid-term, sir?"

"Of course."

From deep out of Blackburn's great chest rose a cry of anguish. "Oh, sir, if you want me to go down on my knees to you, I will, I will."

Howe looked at him in amazement.

"I will, I will. On my knees, sir. This mustn't, mustn't happen."

He spoke so literally, meaning so very truly that his knees and exactly his knees were involved and seeming to think that he was offering something of tangible value to his teacher, that Howe, whose head had become icy clear in the nonsensical drama, thought, "The boy is mad", and began to speculate fantastically whether something in himself attracted or developed aberration. He could see himself standing absurdly before the Dean and saying: "I've found another. This time it's the vice-president of the Council, the manager of the debating team, and secretary of Quill and Scroll."

One more such discovery, he thought, and he himself would be discovered! And there, suddenly, Blackburn was on his knees with a thump, his huge thighs straining his trousers, his hands outstretched in a great gesture of supplication.

With a cry, Howe shoved back his swivel-chair and it rolled away on its casters half across the little room. Blackburn knelt for a moment to nothing at all, then got to his feet.

Howe rose abruptly. He said: "Blackburn, you will stop acting like an idiot. Dust your knees off, take your paper and get out. You've behaved like a fool and a malicious person. You have half a term to do a decent job. Keep your silly mouth shut and try to do it. Now get out."

Blackburn's head was low. He raised it and there was a pious light in his eyes. "Will you shake hands, sir?" he said. He thrust out his hand.

"I will not," Howe said.

Head and hand sank together. Blackburn picked up his blue-book and walked to the door. He turned and said: "Thank you, sir." His back, as he departed, was heavy with tragedy and stateliness.

4

After years of bad luck with the weather, the college had a perfect day for commencement. It was wonderfully bright, the air so transparent, the wind so brisk that no one could resist talking about it.

As Howe set out for the campus he heard Hilda calling from the backyard. She called, "Professor, professor", and came running to him.

Howe said: "What's this 'professor' business?"

"Mother told me," Hilda said. "You've been promoted. And I want to take your picture."

"Next year," said Howe. "I won't be a professor until next year. And you know better than to call anybody 'professor'."

"It was just in fun," Hilda said. She seemed disappointed.

"But you can take my picture if you want. I won't look much different next year." Still, it was frightening. It might mean that he was to stay in this town all his life.

Hilda brightened. "Can I take it in this?" she said, and touched the gown he carried over his arm.

Howe laughed. "Yes, you can take it in this."

"I'll get my things and meet you in front of Otis," Hilda said. "I have the background all picked out."

On the campus the Commencement crowd was already large. It stood about in eager, nervous little family groups. As he crossed Howe was greeted by a student, capped and gowned, glad of the chance to make an event for his parents by introducing one of his teachers. It was while Howe stood there chatting that he saw Tertan.

He had never seen anyone quite so alone, as though a circle had been woven about him to separate him from the gay crowd on the campus. Not that Tertan was not gay — he was the gayest of all. Three weeks had passed since Howe had last seen him, the weeks of examination, the lazy week before Commencement, and this was now a different Tertan. On his head he wore a panama hat, broad-brimmed and fine, of the shape associated with South American planters. He wore a suit of raw silk, luxurious but yellowed with age and much too tight, and he sported a whangee cane. He walked sedately, the hat tilted at a devastating angle, the stick coming up and down in time to his measured tread. He had, Howe guessed, outfitted himself to greet the day in the clothes of that ruined father whose existence was on record in the Dean's office. Gravely and arrogantly he surveyed the scene — in it, his whole bearing seemed to say, but not of it. With his haughty step, with his flashing eye, Tertan was coming nearer. Howe did not wish to be seen. He shifted his position slightly. When he looked again, Tertan was not in sight. The chapel clock struck the quarter hour. Howe detached himself from his chat and hurried to Otis Hall at the far end of the campus. Hilda had not yet come. He went up into the high portico and, using the glass of the door for a mirror, put on his gown, adjusted the hood on his shoulders and set the mortar-board on his head. When he came down the steps Hilda had arrived.

Nothing could have told him more forcibly that a year had passed than the development of Hilda's photographic possessions from the box camera of the previous fall. By a strap about her neck was hung a leather case, so thick and strong, so carefully stitched and so moulded to its contents that it could only hold a costly camera. The appearance was deceptive, Howe knew, for he had been present at the Aikens' pre-Christmas conference about its purchase. It was only a fairly good domestic camera. Still, it looked very impressive. Hilda carried another leather case from which she drew a collapsible tripod. Decisively she extended each of its gleaming legs and set it up on the path. She removed the camera from its case and fixed it to the tripod. In its compact efficiency the camera almost had a life of its own, but Hilda treated it with easy familiarity, looked into its eye, glanced casually at its gauges. Then from a pocket she took still another leather case and drew from it a small instrument through which she looked first at Howe, who began to feel inanimate and lost, and then at the sky. She made some adjustment on the instrument, then some adjustment on the camera. She swept the scene with her eye, found a spot and pointed the camera in its direction. She walked to the spot, stood on it and beckoned to Howe. With each new leather case, with each new instrument and with each new adjustment she had grown in ease and now she said: "Joe, will you stand here?"

Obediently Howe stood where he was bidden. She had yet another instrument. She took out a tape-measure on a mechanical spool. Kneeling down before Howe, she put the little metal ring of the tape under the tip of his shoe. At her request, Howe pressed it with his toe. When she had measured her distance, she nodded to Howe who released the tape. At a touch, it sprang back into the spool. "You have to be careful if you're going to get what you want," Hilda said. "I don't believe in all this snap-snap-snapping," she remarked loftily. Howe nodded in agreement, although he was beginning to think Hilda's care excessive.

Now at last the moment had come. Hilda squinted into the camera, moved the tripod slightly. She stood to the side, holding the plunger of the shutter-cable. "Ready," she said. "Will you relax, Joseph, please?" Howe realized that he was standing frozen. Hilda stood poised and precise as a setter, one hand holding the cable, the other extended with curled dainty fingers like a dancer's, as if expressing to her subject the precarious delicacy of the moment. She pressed the plunger and there was the click. At once she stirred to action, got behind the camera, turned a new exposure. "Thank you," she said, "Would you stand under that tree and let me do a character study with light and shade?"

The childish absurdity of the remark restored Howe's ease. He went to the little tree. The pattern the leaves made on his gown was just what Hilda was after. He had just taken a satisfactory position when he heard in the unmistakable voice: "Ah, Doctor, having your picture taken?"

Howe gave up the pose and turned to Blackburn who stood on the walk, his hands behind his back, a little too large for his bachelor's gown. Annoyed that Blackburn should see him posing for a character study in light and shade, Howe said irritably: "Yes, having my picture taken."

Blackburn beamed at Hilda. "And the little photographer," he said. Hilda fixed her eyes on the ground and stood closer to her brilliant and aggressive camera. Blackburn, teetering on his heels, his hands behind his back, wholly prelatical and benignly patient, was not abashed at the silence. At last Howe said: "If you'll excuse us, Mr Blackburn, we'll go on with the picture."

"Go right ahead, sir. I'm running along." But he only came closer. "Dr Howe," he said fervently, "I want to tell you how glad I am that I was able to satisfy your standards at last."

Howe was surprised at the hard insulting brightness of his own voice and even Hilda looked up curiously as he said: "Nothing you have ever done has satisfied me and nothing you could ever do would satisfy me, Blackburn."

With a glance at Hilda, Blackburn made a gesture as if to hush Howe — as though all his former bold malice had taken for granted a kind of understanding between himself and his teacher, a secret which must not be betrayed to a third person. "I only meant, sir," he said, "that I was able to pass your course after all."

Howe said: "You didn't pass my course. I passed you out of my course. I passed you without even reading your paper. I wanted to be sure the college would be rid of you. And when all the grades were in and I did read your paper, I saw I was right not to have read it first."

Blackburn presented a stricken face. "It was very bad, sir?"

But Howe had turned away. The paper had been fantastic. The paper had been, if he wished to see it so, mad. It was at this moment that the Dean came up behind Howe and caught his arm. "Hello, Joseph," he said. "We'd better be getting along, it's almost late."

He was not a familiar man, but when he saw Blackburn, who approached to greet him, he took Blackburn's arm too. "Hello, Theodore," he said. Leaning forward on Howe's arm and on Blackburn's, he said: "Hello, Hilda, dear." Hilda replied quietly: "Hello Uncle George."

Still clinging to their arms, still linking Howe and Blackburn, the Dean said: "Another year gone, Joe, and we've turned out another crop. After you've been here a few years, you'll find it reasonably upsetting — you wonder how there can be so many graduating classes while you stay the same. But, of course, you don't stay the same." Then he said, "Well," sharply, to dismiss the thought. He pulled Blackburn's arm and swung him around to Howe. "Have you heard about Teddy Blackburn?" he asked. "He has a job already, before graduation, the first man of his class to be placed." Expectant of congratulations, Blackburn beamed at Howe. Howe remained silent.

"Isn't that good?" the Dean said. Still Howe did not answer and the Dean, puzzled and put out, turned to Hilda. "That's a very fine-looking camera, Hilda." She touched it with affectionate pride.

"Instruments of precision," said a voice. "Instruments of precision." Of the three with joined arms, Howe was the nearest to Tertan, whose gaze took in all the scene except the smile and the nod which Howe gave him. The boy leaned on his cane. The broad-brimmed hat, canting jauntily over his eye, confused the image of his face that Howe had established, suppressed the rigid lines of the ascetic and brought out the baroque curves. It made an effect of perverse majesty.

"Instruments of precision," said Tertan for the last time, addressing no one, making a casual comment to the universe. And it occurred to Howe that Tertan might not be referring to Hilda's equipment. The sense of the thrice-woven circle of the boy's loneliness smote him fiercely. Tertan stood in majestic jauntiness, superior to all the scene, but his isolation made Howe ache with a pity of which Tertan was more the cause than the object, so general and indiscriminate was it.

Whether in his sorrow he made some unintended movement towards Tertan which the Dean checked or whether the suddenly tightened grip on his arm was the Dean's own sorrow and fear, he did not know. Tertan watched them in the incurious way people watch a photograph being taken and suddenly the thought that, to the boy, it must seem that the three were posing for a picture together made Howe detach himself almost rudely from the Dean's grasp.

"I promised Hilda another picture," he announced — needlessly, for Tertan was no longer there, he had vanished in the last sudden flux of visitors who, now that the band had struck up, were rushing nervously to find seats.

"You'd better hurry," the Dean said. "I'll go along, it's getting late for me." He departed and Blackburn walked stately by his side.

Howe again took his position under the little tree which cast its shadow over his face and gown. "Just hurry, Hilda, won't you?" he said. Hilda held the cable at arm's-length, her other arm crooked and her fingers crisped. She rose on her toes and said "Ready", and pressed the release. "Thank you," she said gravely and began to dismantle her camera as he hurried off to join the procession.

COMMENTARY

When Matthew Arnold was discussing "the characters of a high quality of poetry" he contended that these were "far better recognized in the verse of the master, than by being perused in the prose of the critic."[1] A corresponding directive could be given if we are asking "What are the characters of a high quality in the short story?" An appreciation of Lionel Trilling's *Of This Time, Of That Place* will go far to answer the question, for this is a masterpiece. The essence of its greatness is to be found in the quality of its vision and the quality of its expression. What these terms mean will, in some measure, be made plain if the story is compared with a story in a glossy magazine or popular weekly. There you will find a standardized superficial story, as much a mass-produced article as trumpery jewellery; what Trilling writes is marked by individuality and by maturity. The difference lies in the measure of reality, of truth, of "felt life", discernible in *Of This Time, Of That Place*.

Inseparable from the originality and the profundity, the sympathy and the insight of Trilling's story, is the absolute rightness of its rendering. Whether we look at the way it is put together, its "architectonics", or at the tone, quiet yet vibrant, of the telling, we find that distinction that belongs only to the master of his craft.

One further general comment may be made before the story is examined. It will sometimes be found that, though not expressly stated, there is conveyed in a work of art a truth wider than the intrinsic validity of its particular statement. In other words, it has universality. So it will be found with *Of This Time*, for what is written of Howe and Tertan and Blackburn at Dwight College touches on issues of social and moral values that are beyond time and place.

How may we best come to a realization of the excellence of this story? It does not matter very much where we begin. Perhaps you have been most impressed on a first reading by the contrast presented by Tertan and Blackburn. Go back and see how Trilling introduces them. (Note Tertan's physical features; his mannerisms and gestures; his peculiar idiom of expression: are these superficial traits or indicative of something deeper? How is the essential hollowness of Blackburn first indicated and later emphasized?) Gradually Tertan establishes a

[1] Ch. 1. 'The Study of Poetry', *Essays in Criticism*, 2nd series.

hold over us as he does over Howe: with this in mind study carefully his answer to the question "Who I am and why I came to Dwight College?" and his contribution to the discussion of Ibsen's *Ghosts*. (Can you think why Trilling made use of *this* play rather than of some other tragedy?) "What is Tertan?" — the question has a more than ordinary significance and makes us as well as Howe think upon our responsibility towards those who differ from the herd and are therefore accounted mad. (Have you perceived the subtle effect made by Howe's calling Blackburn mad?) Balanced against Tertan is Blackburn — in terms of personality, of status and — a bitter twist, this — of worldly prospects. It is not enough to see the rottenness of Blackburn; you must relate that rottenness to its social context.

Central to the story is Howe. (By what means does Trilling make him a sympathetic figure? How is his fineness matched by firmness? At what point do you most admire him?) His significance, however, is seen only if attention is given to the moral issues by which he is confronted. Relate his dealings with Blackburn to the dilemma of the intellectual and the man of principle in a community which certifies Tertan and honours Blackburn.

The more *Of This Time* is studied, the greater is the delight it affords from the realization of the calculated but unforced relevance of its parts and from the unity provided by the framework of the academic year. Look at the first four paragraphs. What do they all serve to create? Why is Hilda with her camera introduced? How is the critical article in *Life and Letters* made of dramatic importance? (Consider what use is made of it by Tertan and Blackburn respectively.)

Of This Time is a wholly satisfying story. Although it makes no overt appeal to emotion by sentimentality of situation or of style, it engages our feelings simultaneously with our intelligence. Our critical alertness is delighted by the overtones of meaning attaching to deftly introduced phrases like "Instruments of precision" and to the whole story as an image for the situation of some American intellectuals. We perceive the pervasive irony. Our response is also to the pathos aroused by Tertan and to disgust at Blackburn and all he represents. Interpreting the terms appropriately for the short story, we may well find here that "high poetic truth and seriousness" which Arnold postulated as indispensable to work of the finest quality.

10

DYLAN THOMAS

1914-1953

POET, script-writer, declaimer, myth, conversationalist, buffoon. Wrote short stories at first as a kind of extension of his poetry, and rather later, to entertain. The poetic *enfant terrible* of the mid-thirties, who from his first bombshell arrival on the London literary scene provoked adulation and detraction in high quarters, and whose premature death during an American reading-tour released an intemperate flood of both; though in fairness one should add that the vehemence of the detractors has always been in part a reaction against the extravagance of the adulators. No doubt the Dylan Thomas vogue, international as it became, was nourished if not begotten by the myth of bohemianism which grew up around him (he was not a bohemian), and by his more just reputation as an unintellectual unpretentious anti-literary pubman. But all this duly discounted, he remains an author who is bound to endure, if only because he spoke of fundamental things in a most memorable and compelling way.

Thomas was born near Carmarthen two months after the outbreak of the First World War, and grew up in Swansea, these two localities remaining throughout his life the theatre of his imagination. He attended Swansea Grammar School, where his father was Senior English Master, without academic distinction or concern, and having decided early what he wanted to do with his talent he left to become a junior reporter, first in Swansea and then in London. In this profession he would probably not have succeeded, hampered as he was by his inability to learn shorthand; but it was never more than a means to an end, which disclosed itself when he had some poems printed, with due fanfare, in the *Sunday Referee*, was formally discovered as a poet, and became in a moment the most lionized and controversial young writer of the day. Committed most eloquently to canvas by Augustus John; granted oracular status by the *avant garde*; deified by Edith Sitwell — for a raw provincial youth with no connections and not much learning it was a spectacular entrée. This did not, however, make him rich. Indeed, it is doubtful if with his temperament he ever could have been even reasonably well off; certainly he never was reasonably well off. Poetry, in any case, does not pay; and the price of Thomas's integrity as a poet was his irregular drifting life, now a B.B.C. reader, now a writer of film scripts, now an all too casual lecturer, but always hard up, and borrowing. Latterly his name gained currency outside the circle of *cognoscenti*, and his work sold curiously well. Even the people of Wales heard of him; some actually read him. But so slim and sporadic an output (he wrote six poems in his last six years) would not have made the fortune even of a temperate man, and too much of Thomas's later activity, including his celebrated lecture-tours, here and in America, was simply high-class potboiling. His sudden death, which only he seems to have anticipated, necessitated the setting up of a fund for the welfare of his family. He had settled for the last few years of his life in a sea's edge cottage at Laugharne in Carmarthenshire, a village which has now discovered itself to be the Llaregub of *Under Milk Wood*.

Readers coming fresh to Thomas's work, perhaps after a hearing of some such rollicking piece as the one given here, are often understandably baffled by the impenetrableness of most of his early writing. "His early poetry was obscure beyond understanding", declared Edwin Muir roundly; and he added, though it will not do as a generalization, that it "was probably incomprehensible to himself". But the fashion has waned of calling in the subconscious to account for Dylan Thomas, as Muir himself did, and it is now clear that this initial arbitrariness had less impressive origins. It was partly the incoherence of mental indiscipline, partly an obliqueness necessitated by the quite unconventional material Thomas was handling (the physiology, and what one might call the metaphysics, of sex and reproduction), and partly, or perhaps chiefly, a calculated indirectness designed to heighten the vehemence, the continual explosiveness, of the attack. This manner Thomas discarded, or lost, with his adolescent prepossessions. In verse and prose alike he moved nearer lucidity, perhaps at the expense of some of his splendid violence, and in his later prose-writing in particular, prophetic robe, always selfconsciously carried, gave way to the cap and bells. As an entertainer his flamboyant personality, exuberant invention, and verbal ingenuity were ample to carry him through. But the inescapable and telling feature of even this phase of his work is the persistence with which he returns to the same small round of situations and themes, the immediate flush of his enthusiasm when he strikes on them once more, however briefly. Richard Eberhart noted perceptively of Thomas that the key to his personality is "innocence after experience". One might find the key to his work in a condition not uncommon with South Waleans, whether or not they write, the attachment of his imagination to the local conditions of his childhood and adolescence, its slowness to kindle genuinely save when reconstructing them or reflecting upon the pathetic lesson of their evanescence.

Suggested Reading: *Collected Poems* 1934-1952 (1952); *Portrait of the Artist as a Young Dog* (1940); *The Doctor and the Devils* (film script), (1953); *Under Milk Wood* (radio script) (1954); *A Prospect of the Sea* (1955); *Quite Early One Morning* (1955).

*   *   *

The Followers

IT was six o'clock on a winter's evening. Thin, dingy rain spat and drizzled past the lighted street lamps. The pavements shone long and yellow. In squeaking goloshes, with mackintosh collars up and bowlers and trilbies weeping, youngish men from the offices bundled home against the thistly wind —

"Night, Mr Macey."

"Going my way, Charlie?"

"Ooh, there's a pig of a night!"

"Good night Mr Swan." —

and older men, clinging on to the big, black circular birds of their umbrellas, were wafted back, up the gaslit hills, to safe, hot slippered, weather-proof hearths, and wives called Mother, and old, fond, fleabag dogs, and the wireless babbling.

Young women from the offices, who smelt of scent and powder and wet pixie hoods and hair, scuttled, giggling, arm-in-arm, after the hissing trams, and screeched as they splashed their stockings in the puddles rainbowed with oil between the slippery lines.

In a shop window, two girls undressed the dummies:

"Where you going tonight?"

"Depends on Arthur. Up she comes."

"Mind her cami-knicks, Edna ... "

The blinds came down over another window.

A newsboy stood in a doorway, calling the news to nobody, very softly: "Earthquake. Earthquake in Japan."

Water from a chute dripped on to his sacking. He waited in his own pool of rain.

A flat, long girl drifted, snivelling into her hanky, out of a jeweller's shop, and slowly pulled the steel shutters down with a hooked pole. She looked, in the grey rain, as though she were crying from top to toe.

A silent man and woman, dressed in black, carried the wreaths away from the front of their flower shop into the scented deadly darkness behind the window lights. Then the lights went out.

A man with a balloon tied to his cap pushed a shrouded barrow up a dead end.

A baby with an ancient face sat in its pram outside the wine vaults, quiet, very wet, peering cautiously all round it.

It was the saddest evening I had ever known.

A young man, with his arm round his girl, passed by me, laughing; and she laughed back, right into his handsome, nasty face. That made the evening sadder still.

I met Leslie at the corner of Crimea Street. We were both about the same age: too young and too old. Leslie carried a rolled umbrella, which he never used, though sometimes he pressed doorbells with it. He was trying to grow a moustache. I wore a check, ratting cap at a Saturday angle. We greeted each other formally:

"Good evening, old man."

"Evening, Leslie."

"Right on the dot, boy."

"That's right," I said. "Right on the dot."

A plump, blonde girl, smelling of wet rabbits, self-conscious even in that dirty night, minced past on high-heeled shoes. The heels clicked, the soles squelched.

Leslie whistled after her, low and admiring.

"Business first," I said.

"Oh, boy!" Leslie said.

"And she's too fat as well."

"I like them corpulent," Leslie said. "Remember Penelope Bogan? a Mrs too."

"Oh, come on. That old bird of Paradise Alley! How's the exchequer, Les?"

"One and a penny. How you fixed?"

"Tanner."

"What'll it be, then? The Compasses?"

"Free cheese at the Marlborough."

We walked towards the Marlborough, dodging umbrella spokes, smacked by our windy macs, stained by steaming lamplight, seeing the sodden, blown scourings and street-wash of the town, papers, rags, dregs, rinds, fag-ends, balls of fur, flap, float, and cringe along the gutters, hearing the sneeze and rattle of the bony trams and a ship hoot like a fog-ditched owl in the bay, and Leslie said:

"What'll we do after?"

"We'll follow someone," I said.

"Remember following that old girl up Kitchener Street? The one who dropped her handbag?"

"You should have given it back."

"There wasn't anything in it, only a piece of bread-and-jam."

"Here we are," I said.

The Marlborough saloon was cold and empty. There were notices on the damp walls: No Singing. No Dancing. No Gambling. No Peddlers.

"You sing," I said to Leslie, "and I'll dance, then we'll have a game of nap and I'll peddle my braces."

The barmaid, with gold hair and two gold teeth in front, like a well-off rabbit's, was blowing on her nails and polishing them on her black marocain. She looked up as we came in, then blew on her nails again and polished them without hope.

"You can tell it isn't Saturday night," I said. "Evening, Miss. Two pints."

"And a pound from the till," Leslie said.

"Give us your one-and-a-penny, Les," I whispered, and then said aloud: "Anybody can tell it isn't Saturday night. Nobody sick."

"Nobody here to *be* sick," Leslie said.

The peeling, liver-coloured room might never have been drunk in at all. Here, commercials told jokes and had Scotches and sodas with happy, dyed, port-and-lemon women; dejected regulars grew grand and muzzy in the corners, inventing their pasts, being rich, important, and loved; reprobate grannies in dustbin black cackled and nipped; influential nobodies revised the earth; a party, with earrings, called "Frilly Willy" played the crippled piano, which sounded like a hurdy-gurdy playing under water, until the publican's nosey wife said, "No." Strangers came and went, but mostly went. Men from the valleys dropped in for nine or ten; sometimes there were fights; and always there was something doing, some argie-bargie, giggle and bluster, horror or folly, affection, explosion, nonsense, peace, some wild goose flying in the boozy air of that comfortless, humdrum nowhere in the dizzy, ditchwater town at the end of the railway lines. But that evening it was the saddest room I had ever known.

Leslie said, in a low voice: "Think she'll let us have one on tick?"

"Wait a bit, boy," I murmured. "Wait for her to thaw."

But the barmaid heard me, and looked up. She looked clean through me, back through my small history to the bed I was born in, then shook her gold head.

"I don't know what it is," said Leslie as we walked up Crimea street in the rain, "but I feel kind of depressed to-night."

"It's the saddest night in the world," I said.

We stopped, soaked and alone, to look at the stills outside the cinema we called the Itch-pit. Week after week, for years and years, we had sat on the edges of the springless seats there, in the dank but snug, flickering dark, first with toffees and monkey-nuts that crackled for the dumb guns, and then with cigarettes: a cheap special kind that would make a fire-swallower cough up the cinders of his heart. "Let's go in and see Lon Chaney," I said, "and Richard Talmadge and Milton Sills and ... and Noah Beary," I said, "and Richard Dix ... and Slim Summerville and Hoot Gibson."

We both sighed.

"Oh, for our vanished youth," I said.

We walked on heavily, with wilful feet, splashing the passers-by.

"Why don't you open your brolly?" I said.

"It won't open. You try."

We both tried, and the umbrella suddenly bellied out, the spokes tore through the soaking cover; the wind danced its tatters; it wrangled above us in the wind like a ruined, mathematical bird. We tried to tug it down: an unseen, new spoke sprang through its ragged ribs. Leslie dragged it behind him, along the pavement, as though he had shot it.

A girl called Dulcie, scurrying to the Itch-pit, sniggered "Hallo," and we stopped her.

"A rather terrible thing has happened," I said to her. She was so silly that, even when she was fifteen, we had told her to eat soap to make her straw hair crinkle, and Les took a piece from the bathroom, and she did.

"I know," she said, "you broke your gamp."

"No, you're wrong there," Leslie said. "It isn't *our* umbrella at all. It fell off the roof. *You* feel," he said. "You can feel it fell off the roof." She took the umbrella gingerly by its handle.

"There's someone up there throwing umbrellas down," I said. "It may be serious."

She began to titter, and then grew silent and anxious as Leslie said: "You never know. It might be walking-sticks next."

"Or sewing-machines," I said.

"You wait here, Dulce, and we'll investigate," Leslie said.

We hurried on down the street, turned a blowing corner, and then ran.

Outside Rabiotti's café, Leslie said: "It isn't fair on Dulcie." We never mentioned it again.

A wet girl brushed by. Without a word, we followed her. She

cantered, long-legged, down Inkerman Street and through Paradise Passage, and we were at her heels.

"I wonder what's the point in following people," Leslie said, "it's kind of daft. It never gets you anywhere. All you do is follow them home and then try to look through the window and see what they're doing and mostly there's curtains anyway. I bet nobody else does things like that."

"You never know," I said. The girl turned into St Augustus Crescent, which was a wide lamplit mist. "People are always following people. What shall we call her?"

"Hermione Weatherby," Leslie said. He was never wrong about names. Hermione was fey and stringy, and walked like a long gym-mistress, full of love, through the stinging rain.

"You never know. You never know what you'll find out. Perhaps she lives in a huge house with all her sisters — "

"How many?"

"Seven. All full of love. And when she gets home they all change into kimonos and lie on divans with music and whisper to each other and all they're doing is waiting for somebody like us to walk in, lost, and then they'll all chatter round us like starlings and put us in kimonos too, and we'll never leave the house until we die. Perhaps it's so beautiful and soft and noisy — like a warm bath full of birds … '

"I don't want birds in my bath," said Leslie. "Perhaps she'll slit her throat if they don't draw the blinds. I don't care what happens so long as it's interesting."

She slip-slopped round a corner into an avenue where the neat trees were sighing and the cosy windows shone.

"I don't want old feathers in the tub," Leslie said.

Hermione turned in at number thirteen, Beach-view.

"You can see the beach all right," Leslie said, "if you got a peri-scope."

We waited on the pavement opposite, under a bubbling lamp, as Hermione opened her door, and then we tiptoed across and down the gravel path and were at the back of the house, outside an uncurtained window.

Hermione's mother, a round, friendly, owlish woman in a pinafore, was shaking a chip-pan on the kitchen stove.

"I'm hungry," I said.

"Ssh!"

We edged to the side of the window as Hermione came into the kitchen. She was old, nearly thirty, with a mouse-brown shingle and big earnest eyes. She wore horn-rimmed spectacles and a sensible, tweed costume, and a white shirt with a trim bow-tie. She looked as though she tried to look like a secretary in domestic films, who had only to remove her spectacles and have her hair cherished, and be dressed like silk dog's dinner, to turn into a dazzler and make her employer, Warner Baxter, gasp, woo, and marry her; but if Hermione took off her glasses, she wouldn't be able to tell if he was Warner Baxter or the man who read the meters.

We stood so near the window, we could hear the chips spitting.

"Have a nice day in the office, dear? There's weather," Hermione's mother said, worrying the chip-pan.

"What's *her* name, Les?"

"Hetty."

Everything there in the warm kitchen, from the tea-caddy and the grandmother clock, to the tabby that purred like a kettle, was good, dull, and sufficient.

"Mr Truscot was something awful," Hermione said as she put on her slippers.

"Where's her kimono?" Leslie said.

"Here's a nice cup of tea," said Hetty.

"Everything's nice in that old hole," said Leslie, grumbling. "Where's the seven sisters like starlings?"

It began to rain much more heavily. It bucketed down on the black back yard, and the little comfy kennel of a house, and us, and the hidden, hushed town, where, even now, in the haven of the Marlborough, the submarine piano would be tinning "Daisy", and the happy henna'd women squealing into their port.

Hetty and Hermione had their supper. Two drowned boys watched them enviously.

"Put a drop of Worcester on the chips," Leslie whispered; and by God she did.

"Doesn't anything happen anywhere?" I said, "in the whole wide world? I think the *News of the World* is all made up. Nobody murders no one. There isn't any sin any more, or love, or death, or pearls and divorces and mink-coats or anything, or putting arsenic in the cocoa...'

"Why don't they put on some music for us," Leslie said, "and do a dance? It isn't every night they got two fellows watching them in the rain. Not *every* night, anyway!"

All over the dripping town, small lost people with nowhere to go and nothing to spend were gooseberrying in the rain outside wet windows, but nothing happened.

"I'm getting pneumonia," Leslie said.

The cat and the fire were purring, grandmother time tick-tocked our lives away. The supper was cleared, and Hetty and Hermione, who had not spoken for many minutes, they were so confident and close in their little lighted box, looked at one another and slowly smiled.

They stood still in the decent, purring kitchen, facing one another.

"There's something funny going to happen," I whispered very softly.

"It's going to begin," Leslie said.

We did not notice the sour, racing rain any more.

The smiles stayed on the faces of the two still, silent women.

"It's going to begin."

And we heard Hetty say in a small secret voice: "Bring out the album, dear."

Hermione opened a cupboard and brought out a big, stiff-coloured photograph album, and put it in the middle of the table. Then she and Hetty sat down at the table, side by side, and Hermione opened the album.

"That's Uncle Eliot who died in Porthcawl, the one who had the cramp," said Hetty.

They looked with affection at Uncle Eliot, but we could not see him.

"That's Martha-the-woolshop, you wouldn't remember her, dear, it was wool, wool, wool, with her all the time; she wanted to be buried in her jumper, the mauve one, but her husband put his foot down. He'd been in India. That's your Uncle Morgan," Hetty said, "one of the Kidwelly Morgans, remember him in the snow?"

Hermione turned a page. "And that's Myfanwy, she got queer all of a sudden, remember. It was when she was milking. That's your cousin Jim, the Minister, until they found out. And that's our Beryl," Hetty said.

But she spoke all the time like somebody repeating a lesson: a well-loved lesson she knew by heart.

We knew that she and Hermione were only waiting.

Then Hermione turned another page. And we knew, by their secret smiles, that this was what they had been waiting for.

"My sister Katinka," Hetty said.

"Auntie Katinka," Hermione said. They bent over the photograph.

"Remember that day in Aberystwyth, Katinka?" Hetty said softly. "The day we went on the choir outing."

"I wore my new white dress," a new voice said.

Leslie clutched at my hand.

"And a straw hat with birds," said the clear, new voice.

Hermione and Hetty were not moving their lips.

"I was always a one for birds on my hat. Just the plumes of course. It was August the third, and I was twenty-three."

"Twenty-three come October, Katinka," Hetty said.

"That's right, love," the voice said. "Scorpio I was. And we met Douglas Pugh on the Prom and he said: 'You look like a queen to-day, Katinka,' he said. 'You look like a queen, Katinka,' he said. Why are those two boys looking in at the window?"

We ran up the gravel drive, and around the corner of the house, and into the avenue and out on to St Augustus Crescent. The rain roared down to drown the town. There we stopped for breath. We did not speak or look at each other. Then we walked on through the rain. At Victoria corner, we stopped again.

"Good night, old man," Leslie said.

"Good night," I said.

And we went our different ways.

COMMENTARY

This piece invites comparison with James Stephens's little farce (pp. 30-40). Like that, the story is told through the mouth of a boy — though an older boy. Like that again, it is very loosely put together, and — until the climax — hardly at all dependent on sheer incident for its comic effect. Both stories stand markedly apart from most others in this book, partly because of the sort of milieu and outlook with which the author identifies himself, and partly because there is an exhilarating air of bravado about them, an exuberance of invention which thrives on the extravagant. Otherwise, it is their differences which are illuminating. Stephens's story is pure farce, and he never for a moment blurs his effect with extraneous overtones; it is a highly professional performance. Thomas was a professional writer too, but he stands much nearer his material. Writing, for him, remained first and foremost a personal fulfilment and release. (Is Thomas's story more tightly constructed than Stephens's or less? How do they differ in structure? In which does incident count for more in itself? Would a bald summary of Thomas's story amount to much?)

On the face of it, Thomas has set himself a daunting task. Adolescent depression is not in itself very momentous, least of all to the adolescent, and a faithful record of it cannot get far away from the trivial and the desultory, the petty staleness of commonplace existence. In themselves, these are the last qualities to found a story on. Thomas's immediate problem, then, was to present boredom without being boring; though it is hardly conjecture that his greater concern was to present triviality without being trivial.

Of course, in the upshot the story is at least superbly entertaining; and it is so in large measure because Thomas has mined it in the writing with every conceivable kind of literary squib — it is, to say no more, a journalistic *tour de force*. One notes in passing how his manner is pitched to allow this. Stephens's story depends a good deal on the voice, but it is the unbuttoned voice of the taproom; he catches the brisk throw-away garrulity of common Dublin speech: his is the art which hides art. Thomas asks for virtuoso performance. His more calculated movement is minutely controlled to allow the subtle modulations in speed, inflection, and cadence, which bring up his effects; and he is acutely alert to the excitements, evocative or dramatic, which lurk in the textures and tensions of the speaking voice. If Stephens is the raconteur Thomas is the spellbinder, the bated-breath declaimer always on the edge of incantation. He blazons his brilliance like a vaunt or challenge. His is a highly conscious, not to say self-conscious, performance.

The immediate outcome of Thomas's closer involvement in his story is its richness of texture. Not only is it alive with the varied (perhaps overconsciously varied) enthusiasms of the senses, but through these, or Thomas's imaginative realization of them, it is constantly evocative of atmosphere and mood. Yet it is certainly not a mere vehicle for a display of sensibility. The effect of the presentation is invigorating; indeed the story provides an object lesson in the vivification by sheer inventive verve of the most unspectacular material. One's attention is unusually drawn, in fact, to the minutiae of the writer's technique. By what specific means does Thomas contrive an attack so warming to the imagination and yet at the same time so boisterously comic? Three aspects of the piece invite immediate attention: the selection of material, the handling of it, and the attitudes portrayed or displayed.

Selection. What is the proportion of descriptive material in the story? Look at Thomas's choice of things to describe in the non-narrative portions: is this entirely random? Is the order of presentation random? If not, on what principle does he make this choice and order — what *kind* of thing does he look for and what is the effect of his arranging it as he does? (For example, does he select ordinary details, or extraordinary and unlikely ones? Would you say that he relies for his effects on the fantastic? the wildly unlikely? the improbable? the grotesque? the absurd? the commonplace? the likely but odd? the likely but angled, or tendentious? Does he achieve anything merely by the *collocation* of things or incidents? Does he "build up" descriptive or dramatic effects at all? If so, how? Is there any pattern in the way he presents sense-impressions — what senses does he use, and to what effect? Are the impressions of any particular sense recorded with unusual accuracy or evocativeness? Is there any marked distortion of sense-impressions? Overall, would a cine-camera record of this particular night in Swansea be preferable to Thomas's description of it? How does this description compare with Joyce's treatment of Dublin scenes in *A Painful Case*?)

Handling. Take any three or four effects which seem to you particularly successful. What makes them so? In the handling of sense-impressions in particular, how much is owed to vivid accuracy of observation, and how much to the originality of the way Thomas has presented it? (Select a few examples for close scrutiny.) Would you say that Thomas's general method of presentation is naturalistic? fanciful? exaggerated? surrealist? impressionistic? Is "truth" a word you would use of much of the writing here? (List some features which might justly be termed truthful. To what are they truthful — the thing as it actually is, or the feelings of someone experiencing it in that particular situation?) Are there any features which must be literally inaccurate or untrue, as Thomas renders them, but which could none the less be said to have another kind of truth — for example, emotional or imaginative truth? To what extent does Thomas rely on surprise, whether in description or narrative? (Are there any effects which seem to you at once unexpected and precisely apt?) Thomas writes about a dispirited frolic in a drab town on a depressing evening: does he manage to convey these three qualities? By what means? If he does, why is his story not dispirited, drab, and depressing, but actually the reverse of this?

What part does imagery play in enlivening the writing? figurative ingenuity? verbal dexterity? comic absurdity? Is there any striking use of the sounds and textures of words, and of aural effects in general? of rhythm and cadence? of epithets? of verbs? (Look for examples of all these, and try to weigh their effect.)

Attitudes. Do you think Thomas enjoyed writing this? What evidence is there that he did? Does the story seem to you to have any autobiographical truth? The town is unmistakably Swansea, Thomas's boyhood home: do you think he had any affection for it?

Look at the snapshot-characters in the early part of the story: does Thomas hit them off in the brief glimpses he affords us? Are Dulcie Protheroe, "Hermione" and "Hetty", recognizable types? Are they stock *literary* types, or genuine observations of people? Is Auntie Katinka a stock type? Would you say that the two women in the kitchen are purely comic figures? Their conversation is very commonplace and careworn — what makes it funny?

Does Thomas intend to satirize or in any way criticize the two boys, or does he show wholehearted sympathy and support for them? Might the truth be somewhere between these — an amused indulgence? If so, to what in particular about them is he indulgent? How is it that the dejection of the boys becomes very funny? Does "too young and too old" say anything true about them? If so, what? They are obviously more sophisticated than Stephens's protagonist in that they consciously strike attitudes to themselves, each other, and the world about them: what are these attitudes, and where does Thomas reveal them? What attitude emerges in the remark, "Oh, for our vanished youth!"? How would you characterize their actual attitude (as distinct from their pose) to people and circumstances — is it, for example, accepting? resigned? apathetic? timorous? truculent? brash? obstinate? malicious? rebellious? superior? inferior? irreverent? awestruck? subservient? Are the two boys differentiated at all, in their attitudes or speech? How does the cockiness these boys display differ from that shown by James Stephens's boy — is the difference something to do with their age? Is there anything in the story which suggests that behind their bounce is a dejected consciousness of their own unimportance in a largely disapproving world? Could it be that their dogged mutinous-ness is really a half-hearted attempt to fight back against that world by kicking against its proprieties and conventions? Would this be a true observation of adolescence? Does Thomas show any understanding of adolescent behaviour in general, or is his account the usual adult falsification of the state? What features, if any, seem to you to show especial insight (their effect might be comic, of course)? It is a usual experience that this story succeeds explosively with adolescent boys, who will often continue to reproduce bits of it in their own work for some time: what might account for this special appeal?

We have reserved the final episode. Up to the last page of the story Thomas is writing of common, not to say commonplace occurrences. His "I" might well have been himself some twenty years back; indeed, there is a nostalgic warmth and truth about the whole evocation which suggests that it was written quite directly out of his own general experience. Possibly one of the most telling successes of the story is its cheerful exposé of normal attitudes which are not politely admissible or admitted: adolescents do have lavish erotic day-dreams, do follow girls, do stare furtively through uncurtained windows. But however authentic Thomas's narrative up to that point, what is beyond doubt is that the climax never occurred as he describes it. Quite apart from the likelihood of any such ghostly intervention, it is not possible that a quiet conversation in a closed room should be audible outside the window at all, much less intelligible amid the hubbub of frying within and heavy rain without. Evidently this is a shift contrived to clinch the story; some would say a typically cheap shift, which exposes the ultimate irresponsibility of Thomas's art.

Actually, one's experience is that it is not the implausibility of the episode which first strikes a sympathetic reader, but its truth. That is simple, but quite fundamental. What is the poignancy of a photograph, a snapshot in particular? In it, the casual trivia of the instant are almost arbitrarily salvaged from time — "immortalized in a moment" as Thomas himself puts it elsewhere — and made the index of man's impermanence. Nor is this momentary rehearsal of the emotion which pulses through all Dylan Thomas's later writing any the less trenchant because he here delicately balances pathos with absurdity, as it often is balanced in human affairs. Dead Auntie Katinka, fixed for ever on the prom. at Aberystwyth in the smiles and finery of her holidaying youth, is a stock figure of fun; but there is more than a local inquietude in the snapshot's pitiful adumbration of the emotions of that long-vanished day when she, a young girl with the life before her that is now wholly gone, met Douglas Pugh on the choir-outing and he praised her unforgettably.

Possibly the heart of the whole matter is the conclusion of that *Return Journey to Swansea* Thomas made in search not only of the town he remembered, since war-savaged, but of the "Young Thomas" who once swore and swaggered there: "dead, dead, dead".

(Take the whole final episode in the kitchen. By what means is (*a*) the atmosphere of the room suggested (*b*) the dramatic climax prepared? Examine in detail the mingling of comedy and pathos here. What, if anything, makes these effects congruous? How does the episode compare in this respect with the last dialogue between Captain Cat and Rosie Probert in *Under Milk Wood*? What other writers — or performers — do you know who sometimes blend comedy and pathos? Do you recall any celebrated scenes in plays or novels which get some part of their appeal from such a blend? What *is* pathos?

Does this last episode emerge organically from the whole development of the story? Is it generally in keeping with the rest? Or does it just seem arbitrarily stuck on to provide an ending?)

ACKNOWLEDGMENTS

Acknowledgment and thanks for permission to reprint copyright matter are due to the following authors, executors and publishers:

Mrs Stephens and Messrs. Macmillan & Co. Ltd. for A RHINOCEROS, SOME LADIES, AND A HORSE by James Stephens. Messrs. Martin Secker & Warburg Ltd. for SHOOTING AN ELEPHANT by George Orwell. Messrs. J. M. Dent & Sons Ltd. for THE FOLLOWERS from *A Prospect of the Sea by Dylan Thomas.* Mrs M. Caradoc Evans for BE THIS HER MEMORIAL by Caradoc Evans. The Estate of the late Mrs Frieda Lawrence and Messrs. William Heinemann Ltd. for TICKETS, PLEASE from *The Complete Short Stories of D. H. Lawrence.* The Author and Messrs. Jonathan Cape Ltd. for THE MOWER from *The Bride Comes to Evensford and Other Tales* by H. E. Bates. The Executors of the James Joyce Estate and Messrs. Jonathan Cape Ltd. for A PAINFUL CASE from *Dubliners* by James Joyce. The Macmillan Co., New York, and A. D. Peters for IN THE TRAIN from *Bones of Contention* by Frank O'Connor. The Estate of the late Henry James for PASTE by Henry James. Lionel Trilling, Esq., for OF THIS TIME, OF THAT PLACE.